North Dakota's Polar Pilot

OTHER BOOKS BY KEVIN KREMER:

A Kremer Christmas Miracle

Spaceship Over North Dakota

Saved by Custer's Ghost

The Blizzard of the Millennium

When it Snows in Sarasota

Santa's Our Substitute Teacher

Are You Smarter Than a Flying Gator

Maggie's Christmas Miracle

The Year Our Teacher Won the Super Bowl

The Most Amazing Halloween Ever

Are You Smarter Than a Flying Teddy

Angel of the Prairie

The Worst Day of School EVER—Do-Over

Valentine Shmellentine

Captain Grant Marsh

North Dakota's Polar Pilot

The Heroic Story of Carl Ben Eielson from Hatton

by Paulette Bullinger and Kevin Kremer

Published by Kremer Publishing
2022
P.O. Box 1385
Osprey, FL 34229-1385

www.KevinKremerBooks.com

Kremer Publishing
P.O. Box 1385
Osprey, FL 34229-1385

Visit us on the web! KevinKremerBooks.com

ISBN: 978-1-7333492-6-0

First Edition

Book design by Elisabeth Arena 2022

The photo on the next page is from the State Historical Society of North Dakota

The photo on the back cover was taken by the author at the Theodore Roosevelt Rough Rider Hall of Fame at the State Capitol in Bismarck, North Dakota

The photos on pages 170 and 171 are Shutterstock photos

Carl Ben Eielson

Dedication

This book is dedicated to Ruth Chase, Bob Chase, and Jim Lawler, three people who were instrumental in helping the Mandan Municipal Airport thrive for almost 60 years.

Ruth Chase, Mandan Airport bookkeeper, 1962-1988, and Bob Chase, General Manager 1962-1988

Jim Lawler: Mechanic and Grounds Assistant, 1980-1988; General Manager, 1988-2020

Special thanks to:

*Pilot Logan Rubbert, who gave author Paulette Bullinger a thrilling experience during her first small airplane ride as she took aerial photos of Hatton, North Dakota, and even landed in a field nearby.

Pilot Logan Rubbert and author, Paulette Bullinger

KAREN BERG

*Karen Berg, who helped immensely with the photo tour of the Hatton-Eielson Museum

*Elisabeth Arena for her great work designing the book

*Alex Stubbs for her awesome cover design

*Super former student, Miranda Dietrich, for taking photos of Carl Ben Eielson Middle School in Fargo.

Contents

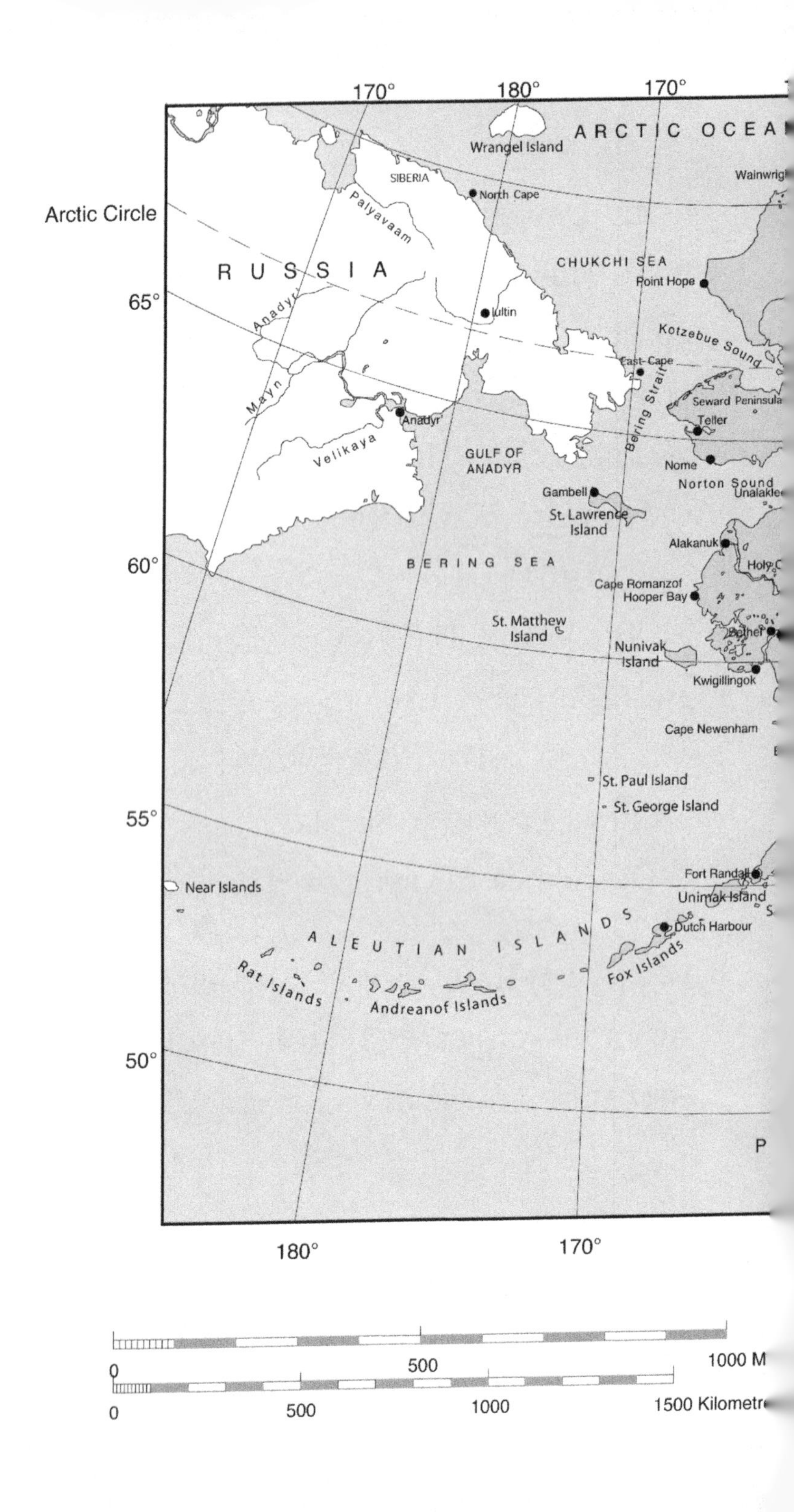
170°
180°
170°
ARCTIC OCEAN
Wrangel Island
SIBERIA
North Cape
Arctic Circle
Palyavaam
RUSSIA
CHUKCHI SEA
Point Hope
65°
Anadyr
Iultin
Kotzebue Sound
East Cape
Bering Strait
Seward Peninsula
Mayn
Anadyr
Teller
Velikaya
GULF OF ANADYR
Nome
Norton Sound
Gambell
St. Lawrence Island
Alakanuk
60°
BERING SEA
Cape Romanzof
Hooper Bay
St. Matthew Island
Bethel
Nunivak Island
Kwigillingok
Cape Newenham
St. Paul Island
St. George Island
55°
Fort Randall
Near Islands
Unimak Island
Dutch Harbour
ALEUTIAN ISLANDS
Rat Islands
Andreanof Islands
Fox Islands
50°
P
180°
170°
0
500
1000 M
0
500
1000
1500 Kilometr

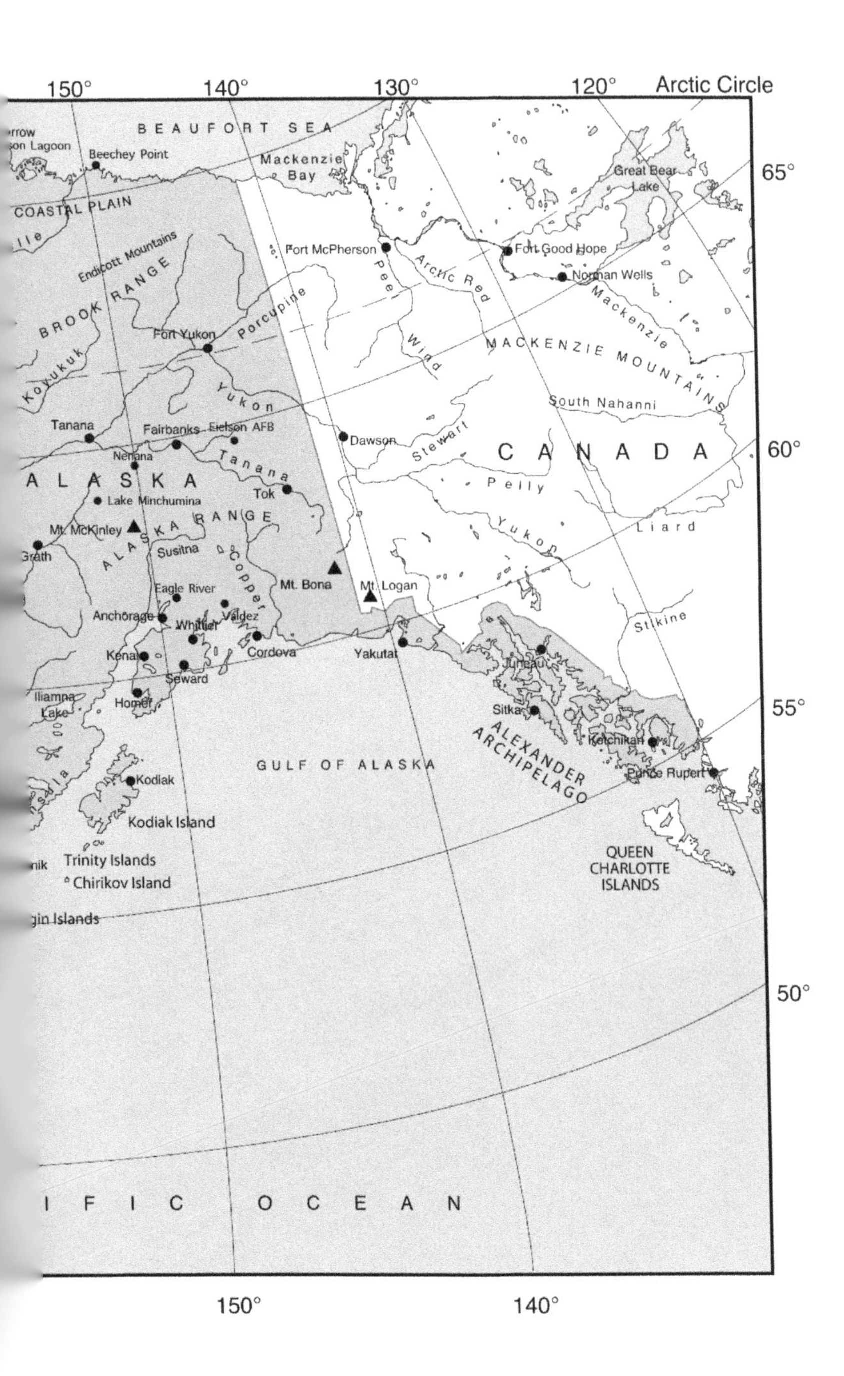

150°
140°
130°
120°
Arctic Circle
BEAUFORT SEA
Beechey Point
Mackenzie Bay
Great Bear Lake
65°
COASTAL PLAIN
Endicott Mountains
BROOK RANGE
Fort McPherson
Fort Good Hope
Norman Wells
Peel
Arctic Red
Porcupine
Fort Yukon
Mackenzie
Wind
MACKENZIE MOUNTAINS
Koyukuk
Yukon
South Nahanni
Tanana
Fairbanks
Eielson AFB
Dawson
Stewart
CANADA
60°
Nenana
ALASKA
Tanana
Tok
Pelly
Lake Minchumina
ALASKA RANGE
Mt. McKinley
Liard
Yukon
Susitna
Copper
Mt. Bona
Mt. Logan
Eagle River
Anchorage
Whittier
Valdez
Stikine
Kenai
Cordova
Yakutat
Juneau
Seward
Iliamna Lake
Homer
Sitka
55°
ALEXANDER ARCHIPELAGO
Ketchikan
GULF OF ALASKA
Prince Rupert
Kodiak
Kodiak Island
Trinity Islands
Chirikov Island
QUEEN CHARLOTTE ISLANDS
50°
OCEAN
150°
140°

CHAPTER 1

Blizzard Day

"Kinley! Thomas!" Mother called from the bottom of the steps. "They've canceled school for tomorrow!"

Eleven-year-old Kinley and her ten-year-old brother, Thomas, rushed out of their bedrooms and down the stairs, where their parents were waiting for them.

Their dad had a smile on his face. "There's a big blizzard coming into North Dakota from Montana."

"May we call Grandpa?" Kinley asked excitedly.

"Grandpa will probably be calling *you* in the next few minutes," said Mother. "No one has more fun than the three of you on Blizzard Days."

As if on cue, the phone rang.

Mother chuckled. "It's Grandpa!" she said.

Sure enough, it was.

Kinley and Thomas felt so blessed that their grandpa lived in Mandan, and they lived in Bismarck, just seven miles away on the other side of the Missouri River. They had so much fun spending time with their grandpa, and those rare Blizzard Days when school was canceled were always extra special.

An hour later, Grandpa knocked on the front door and came inside. At six feet four inches, Grandpa's head barely cleared the doorway. He was wearing blue jeans and his brown leather jacket. He had a Pittsburgh Steelers cap covering most of his full head of black and gray curly hair.

"Hi, everyone!" he said with his booming, friendly, enthusiastic voice.

Kinley and Thomas ran over to greet their Grandpa with big hugs.

"Hi, Grandpa!" said Kinley.

"Hi, Grandpa!" said Thomas.

"Do you two have everything you need?" Grandpa asked.

"Yup," answered Kinley. "Dad double-checked our duffles."

Mother was next to give Grandpa a big hug.

"Thanks for doing this again, Dad," she said.

Grandpa smiled. "I need to thank *you*, Sarah. Some of my favorite memories involve Blizzard Days with Kinley and Thomas. Now, we have a chance to make even more great memories."

Father came over and shook Grandpa's hand. "How's it going, Mike?" he asked.

"Great!" Grandpa replied. "Thanks for letting me take the kids for the next few days. I promise we will do everything safely as always."

"I know you will," said Father. "Sarah and I will

probably need to work from home the next couple of days, but we'll try to have a little fun too."

"We'll stay in touch," said Grandpa.

Kinley and Thomas picked up their duffle bags and snowmobile suits.

"Have a great time!" said Mother.

"Save a few cookies for us," added Father.

"We will," said Thomas.

Grandpa, Kinley, and Thomas went outside and got into the warm cab of Grandpa's truck as light snow fell from the sky. As they were traveling on Interstate 94 to Mandan, Kinley said, "Grandpa, do you have another great blizzard story to tell us this time?"

Grandpa smiled. "Yup," he said. "It's going to be tough to top the blizzard story I told you last March about Hazel Miner, but I think I have another story you two will like a lot. It's not really a blizzard story, but it definitely has some blizzards involved—plus some of the coldest weather in the world."

"Awesome," said Thomas. "How did you find out about this story, Grandpa?"

"It was a surprise," Grandpa replied. "I was having coffee and waffles at the Copper Dog Café with some friends, and they were talking about the first Mandan Airport, built way back in 1933. I'd never even heard of it. They said it was located a little south of the east end of what we used to call *The Strip*—the old road between Bismarck and Mandan. It wasn't too far from where the Memorial Bridge is located. My friends knew the name of the airport, but they didn't really know anything else. That's when I started to get interested in the man the airport was named after."

Copper Dog Café in Mandan; *Author Photo*

"What was the name of the airport?" asked Kinley.

"It was called Eielson Field," said Grandpa. "It was named after a great man with a great story—a man named Carl Ben Eielson (EYE-ull-son)."

"Why did they name it after *him*?" asked Thomas. "Did he fly airplanes or something?"

"He sure did," replied Grandpa. "He flew airplanes when flying airplanes was a pretty new thing. I think I've got a few good photos of Carl Ben flying one of his planes on my phone that will give you a little hint."

Grandpa showed them the photos.

"Please start telling the story," Kinley pleaded.

"I'll tell you what," said Grandpa. "We'll stop up here at one of your favorite places for some lunch, and we can get started with the story while we're eating."

"Where are we going?" Kinley asked.

State Historical Society of North Dakota

Grandpa looked over at his grandkids with a twinkle in his eye. "Anyone up for some fleischkuekle (flysh-keek-la) and knoephla (nef-la) soup?"

"We're going to Frieds!" said Kinley excitedly.

"I love Frieds!" Thomas exclaimed.

"Yup!" said Grandpa. "Frieds it is!"

CHAPTER 2

Frieds Restaurant

FRIEDS RESTAURANT IN NORTH MANDAN; *AUTHOR PHOTO*

Owners Tracey and Julie Gegelman were working in the kitchen when Grandpa, Kinley, and Thomas entered the restaurant.

"Good morning, Mike, Kinley, and Thomas!" Tracey exclaimed when he saw the three of them come in.

Julie smiled. "I'm guessing you three are having another one of your Blizzard Day celebrations," she said.

"Yup," Grandpa answered. "We thought we'd load up on some fleischkuekle (flysh-keek-la) and knoephla (nef-la) soup to get us started. If we have room, maybe we'll even have a piece of your fantastic cherry pie."

"I love your Blizzard Day get-togethers," said Julie. "Who would have thought a North Dakota blizzard could be so much fun?"

"What are some of the things you've got planned?" asked Tracey.

Thomas said, "We will do some of our favorites, like building snow tunnels and making Great Aunt Karol's chocolate chip cookies—and Grandpa said he has another great story to tell us."

"What fun!" said Julie. "Would you please save one of those cookies for us?"

"We sure will," said Kinley.

Tracey said, "I think your favorite booth is available, and Lydia is working this morning. She'll be happy to see you three again."

Lydia heard them talking, and she suddenly appeared with a big smile on her face. Lydia was one of the friendliest waitresses in the world, and you could tell she loved her job.

"It's so great to see my three favorite customers!" Lydia said enthusiastically, hugging each of them. "Let me take you to your booth."

When Grandpa, Kinley, and Thomas were seated, Lydia said, "Now, let me guess—you want fleischkuekle and knoephla soup, plus a large order of fries you can share—maybe some pie for later. Coffee for Mike and milk for Kinley and Thomas."

"That's perfect," said Kinley.

"I'll be back in a jiffy," said Lydia.

"Grandpa," said Kinley, "I think you told us once about some of the history of fleischkuekle and knoephla soup, but I don't remember much of it."

Thomas said, "Didn't they both have something to do with the Germans from Russia that settled in North Dakota?"

"That's right, Thomas," said Grandpa. "The Germans from Russia brought both foods to North Dakota. Many of your ancestors were actually part of that large group of Germans from Russia that came to the United States beginning in the late 1860s."

"Why did they move here?" asked Kinley.

"I guess the simple answer is, they were looking for a better way of life," said Grandpa. "They had left Germany and gone to Russia way back in 1762 when the empress of Russia named Catherine the Great offered them free land to farm and other things like freedom of religion. They could also keep their German language and customs. Then, about 100 years after that, in the 1860s, a new leader of Russia decided he didn't want the Germans in Russia anymore. They had to either leave the country or the men would be forced to fight in a war against their native country of Germany and probably be killed. Because of that, more than 200,000 of those Germans from Russia fled to the United States and Canada. About 31,000 of them were in North Dakota by 1910, including many of your ancestors."

"Why did so many of them come to North Dakota?" asked Thomas.

"They loved the freedom they would have, and there was lots of land available," said Grandpa. "Also, the climate wasn't much different than what it was in Germany, so their farming practices worked well here. The Germans from Russia were hardworking people, so they thrived."

Lydia brought them their beverages with a friendly smile. "Here you go," she said. "I'll be back with your food in a few minutes."

"Thanks, Lydia," said Grandpa.

Kinley said, "Grandpa, do you know where the names *fleischkuekle* and *knoephla* come from?"

"I think the word *knoephla* comes from a German word meaning *knob* or *button*, and that's what the little pieces of dough kind of look like in the soup, but I don't know anything about where *fleischkuekle* comes from. We can do some research on that later if you'd like."

Kinley said, "Grandpa, could you start telling us your story about Carl Ben now? … How did you pronounce his last name again?"

"It's Carl Ben EYE-ull-son," said Grandpa. "The last name is Norwegian. I read that Carl Ben's parents named him Carl Benjamin, but they usually called him *Ben*. Other people called him Carl Ben or Benjamin, and I'm going to use Carl Ben. Let me give you some background first because it's really important, and I think it's really interesting too."

"Carl Ben EYE-ull-son?" Kinley tried.

"That's good," said Grandpa. "So, for this story, let's imagine turning the clock back to the day Carl Ben was born on July 20, 1897. What a different world it was back then. … North Dakota had only been a state for about eight years. If you wanted to travel between Mandan and

Bismarck back then, you'd have to take a train or a boat to cross the Missouri River. Steamboats were still operating on the rivers. Back in 1897, there were automobiles, but they were expensive and not very safe and reliable, and the roads weren't very good either. Henry Ford's Model Ts wouldn't come off the assembly line until 1908."

"Who was president?" asked Thomas.

"William McKinley was the 25th president of the United States," replied Grandpa, "and Teddy Roosevelt would become president in about four more years."

"And there wouldn't be any Pittsburgh Steelers football for about 36 more years," said Thomas.

Kinley chuckled. "I knew the Steelers were going to come up in this conversation."

"Here's something else that was pretty interesting about life back then," said Grandpa. "Carl Ben liked playing basketball, like the three of us do. Well, basketball was invented by James Naismith in 1891, just six years before Carl Ben was born. Carl Ben used to talk about playing basketball by throwing a ball into a fruit basket when he was a kid."

"And James Naismith used peach baskets when he invented the game," Thomas added.

"Pretty cool," said Kinley.

Grandpa said, "There was something else that happened not long after Carl Ben was born that is an important part of this story. The Wright Brothers made their famous flight in late 1903, when Carl Ben was just six years old. And as a young boy, Carl Ben started dreaming about flying himself."

James Naismith; *Author's Collection*

Wright Brothers' Flight, 1903; *Author's Collection*

CHAPTER 3

Lutefisk! Oh My!

"Here you go," said Lydia, placing the food on the table with a friendly smile.

"It smells so good!" said Thomas.

"Thanks, Lydia!" added Kinley.

"You're the best, Lydia!" said Grandpa.

"You are all so very welcome," said Lydia.

"Lydia, do you know where the word *fleischkuekle* (flysh-keek-la) comes from?" asked Kinley.

Lydia said, "I always thought it meant *meat pie* in some German dialect, but I'm not sure. If you have a chance to research it sometime, please let me know what you find out."

"We will," Kinley replied.

Grandpa said, "Lydia, we hope to have room for a piece of pie when we're done with all this food, but we'll have to see if our eyes are bigger than our stomachs."

"Excellent," said Lydia. "I'll be back in a few minutes and check up on you."

"Thanks again," said Thomas.

"You're so welcome."

Fleischkuekle from Frieds; *Author Photo*

Knoephla Soup from Frieds; *Author Photo*

As they started eating, Kinley asked, "Grandpa, do you think Carl Ben ate any fleischkuekle or knoephla soup?"

Grandpa chuckled. "Remember, I mentioned before, the name *Eielson* was Norwegian. Well, I read about Carl Ben eating some Norwegian foods. ... Almost a million Norwegians came to America looking for a better way of life in the late 19th and early 20th centuries. Carl Ben's grandparents came to Minnesota from Norway, then they moved to North Dakota, and I can tell you this. Most of those Norwegians who moved to North Dakota probably ate two foods that many Norwegians I know *still* like to eat and talk about. I'm guessing Carl Ben only liked one of them, though—a delicious potato flatbread called *lefse* (LEF-suh)."

"We had some of that at Christmas time," said Thomas. "I love that."

"Me too," said Kinley.

Suddenly, Grandpa made a funny *icky face* and said, "The other Norwegian food that's talked about a lot is one of the most notorious, disgusting foods I've encountered in my entire life in North Dakota, and it's hard for me to believe *anyone* could possibly eat it. It smells bad, it looks bad, and it tastes bad—but some of my friends actually like it a lot! It's called *lutefisk* (LOO-tuh-fisk)."

"Yikes! What is it?" asked Kinley.

"Let me start with the smell first," said Grandpa. "They used to have a dinner at the Lutheran Church in Mandan that served lefse and lutefisk—and let me tell you! All we could smell, even though our house was one block away from the church, was that *lutefisk*. Too me, it was a little like smelling a combination of rotten fish and stinky feet."

Thomas and Kinley both started laughing.

"It can't be *that* bad," said Kinley.

"Oh, yes, it is!" Grandpa exclaimed. "It might be even

worse!"

"But what is it?" asked Thomas.

"Lutefisk is basically fish soaked in a liquid called *lye* to preserve it. Lye is a poison, but I guess it becomes harmless once it's cooked. And when the lutefisk is done cooking, it is really revolting! My mother encouraged me to try it at one of the Lutheran Church dinners, but I couldn't. The smell was so bad—how could it possibly taste any good?" Grandpa made that *icky face* again. "I mean, after it's cooked, it looks like a slippery, jiggly, squishy, translucent pile of gunk. Then people often cover it with lots of butter before they eat it."

"Wow!" said Kinley, giggling. "It sounds even worse than the head cheese and sardines you eat."

Grandpa gave Kinley a serious look, then he laughed. "Kinley, don't you go making fun of my sardines and head cheese!"

They all laughed some more.

"Do you know how lutefisk got started?" asked Thomas.

"No one seems to know," said Grandpa, "but there are some stories that have come down over the years. My favorite story involves the Vikings and St. Patrick from Ireland. As the story goes, the Vikings were invading Ireland, and St. Patrick tried to poison the Vikings with some lutefisk. But instead of killing them, the Vikings liked it a lot! I guess the story really couldn't be true because St. Patrick lived a long time before the Vikings attacked Ireland, but I like it anyway."

"At least it's a funny story," said Thomas.

Kinley had a mischievous look on her face. "The whole lutefisk thing is too funny," she said. "Could we try making it sometime, Grandpa, so I know if you're exaggerating or not?"

"Not in my house!" said Grandpa with chuckle. "It

would take a year to get that smell out of there."

They all laughed some more.

"You'll both like this," Grandpa added. "There's a town in Minnesota named Madison that calls itself the Lutefisk Capital of the United States. They've even got a big fish named Lou T. Fisk in one of their parks. I think I have a photo of him on my computer at home I can show you."

Lou T. Fisk in Madison, Minnesota; *Photo courtesy of the Madison Area Chamber of Commerce*

"Lou T. Fisk," Thomas repeated. "That's pretty funny."

"Grandpa, you never told us where Carl Ben lived in North Dakota," said Kinley.

"He lived in Hatton, a small town about 40 miles southwest of Grand Forks," Grandpa explained. "Remember when we were talking about all the new towns that sprung up in North Dakota along where the railroads were being built?"

"Yes," replied Kinley.

"Well, those railroads made it possible to bring people and supplies into areas, and that made it easier to live there. Hatton sprung up in rich farming country in the Red River Valley, a great place for people to farm or to work in towns that supplied the farmers. Hatton was made possible by the Great Northern Railroad, and it came into existence in 1881, eight years before North Dakota became a state."

"Where did the name *Hatton* come from?" asked Thomas.

"Hatton was named after an assistant postmaster general of the United States named Frank Hatton. They wanted to name the town *Garfield*, after President James Garfield, but that name was turned down by the government."

"Why?" asked Thomas.

"There was already a *Garfield* in the Dakota Territory at that time."

"What did Carl Ben's mom and dad do in Hatton?" asked Kinley.

"Carl Ben's mom, Olava, was really busy raising a large family," replied Grandpa.

"How many kids were there in the family?" asked Thomas.

"Nine," Grandpa replied. "From oldest to youngest, they were named Elma, Edwin, Carl Ben, Adeline, Oliver, and Arthur … then there were twins named Helen and Hannah. Sadly, Hannah died when she was just a baby, but they had another child after that, and they named her Hannah."

"Do you know anything more about the two Hannahs?" asked Kinley.

"There's quite a bit," replied Grandpa. "I'll save that part of the story for later. But I've got a photo here on my phone of all the kids back in 1907, when Carl Ben would have been about ten. The last three children hadn't been born yet when this photo was taken.

Grandpa showed them the photo.

Eielson children in 1907; L-R: Elma, Arthur, Carl Ben, Adeline, Oliver in front of Adeline, Edwin; *Author's photo, taken at the Hatton-Eielson Museum*

"They're all so cute!" said Kinley.

"I love the way they're dressed," said Thomas. "Is Carl Ben the tall one standing in the middle there wearing what looks like a bow tie?"

"It sure is," replied Grandpa. "I wish I had a photo with all the kids and their parents, too, but I don't. Maybe we can find one later."

"What did Carl Ben's dad do?" asked Thomas.

"Carl Ben's dad, Ole, owned a general store in town, and he also organized a bank in Hatton called the Farmers and Merchants Bank. He also became the mayor of Hatton for 12 years. He was very successful, and the Eielsons moved to a really big house in town after the first five kids were born. I'll show you a photo of it when we get to my house."

"Do you know how Ole and Olava met each other?" asked Kinley.

"Yes, I do," said Grandpa. "Olava Baalson came from Brooten, Minnesota, to visit relatives in Hatton. When she came into the Eielson store to shop, Ole couldn't help but notice the pretty young Olava right away. He was a little nervous, but he asked if he could see her that evening."

"And the rest is history," said Kinley.

"Yup," said Grandpa, "They were married, and they settled in Hatton and started raising that big family."

"What was Carl Ben like when he was growing up?" asked Thomas.

"I'm going to need my computer to tell that part of the story," said Grandpa. "Let's finish eating and go to my house. We can make some cookies and continue the story there."

CHAPTER 4

Great Aunt Karol's Chocolate Chip Cookies

When they got to Grandpa's house on Sunset Drive in Mandan, they all took off their coats and boots. Then Kinley and Thomas hung up their snowmobile suits and took their duffle bags to their rooms. After that, they hustled to the kitchen to start making a big batch of Great Aunt Karol's chocolate chip cookies.

"All right," said Grandpa. "We've done this many times before. Let's get to it."

"I'll turn the oven on to 375," said Thomas.

"Grandpa and I will start measuring ingredients and mixing," said Kinley.

Thomas asked, "Grandpa, is there any chance Carl Ben got to eat chocolate chip cookies when he was a boy?"

Grandpa replied, "Remember Thomas, Carl Ben was born in 1897. Do you remember when chocolate chip cookies were invented?"

"I remember," said Kinley. "We went through that when we were talking about Hazel Miner's story last year. Chocolate chip cookies weren't invented until the 1930s, I think?"

"That's right," said Grandpa. "Ruth Wakefield baked the first chocolate chip cookies at the Toll House Restaurant in Whitman, Massachusetts. Sorry, Carl Ben. I'm not sure what growing up would have been without chocolate chip cookies."

"Especially without Great Aunt Karol's!" exclaimed Thomas.

GREAT AUNT KAROL'S CHOCOLATE CHIP COOKIES BAKED BY JENNIFER KREMER HUSCHKA

DETAILED RECIPE IN THE BACK OF THIS BOOK!

After they baked the cookies, Grandpa got his laptop computer and placed it on the kitchen table in front of him. After that, the three of them sat around the kitchen table and started eating the delicious, warm cookies.

"So, let's start talking about Carl Ben growing up," said Grandpa. "I'm not sure how I want to start."

"Please tell us about the two Hannahs in the family," said Kinley.

"I'm going to save that for a little later," said Grandpa, "but please remind me if I forget."

"I will," said Kinley.

"Thanks, Kinley," said Grandpa. "Let me start with the parents, Ole and Olava, because good parents make all the difference in a family, and those Eielson kids had two terrific parents. Both of their parents emphasized the importance of getting a good education and having a strong church life. The whole family went to church together."

"Their family would take up a whole pew," said Kinley.

"That's right," said Grandpa. "On weekdays, Ole was gone most of the day, working hard at the general store, while Olava had a full-time job taking care of all those kids when they weren't in school. I read that Olava encouraged the kids to explore and think for themselves. She made sure there was lots of love and fun in that house, but the kids were well-disciplined, just like you two are."

"Most of the time," said Kinley, giggling.

"I'll bet there was never a dull moment around that house," said Grandpa. "That's one of the great things about growing up in a large family. There's always someone to play with, and there's always something going on. I think those kids were blessed to have had that big house to grow up in. Imagine all the places they could hide when they were playing hide-and-seek in that place. … Oh, I've got a photo of the house on my computer to show you."

Eielson Home in Hatton; *Author Photo*

"I sure would like to walk around in that house someday," said Kinley.

"Me too," said Thomas.

"Maybe we can do that sometime," said Grandpa.

"That would be awesome!" said Kinley. "Besides hide-and-seek, what were some of the other things they did for fun?"

Grandpa said, "I read about them writing and performing their own plays up in the attic, and they played croquet in their yard, just like we do. They climbed the windmill in their yard. They explored caves nearby. In the winter, they ice skated and went snow skiing. In many ways, I think the Eielson kids grew up in better times, when kids didn't spend so much time on their electronic gadgets, and they used their imaginations so much more."

"What was Carl Ben like?" asked Kinley.

Grandpa said, "These are some of the words that were used to describe him: Modest, patient, smart. And he walked and talked in his sleep."

"Just like you, Grandpa," said Thomas.

"Yes, just like I used to do," Grandpa admitted.

"How did Carl Ben get interested in flying in the first place?" asked Kinley.

"I think he probably got interested in flying way before he even heard about the Wright Brothers," said Grandpa. "What kid with a good imagination doesn't think about that when they're little? I sure did."

"Me too," said Thomas.

"Me three," added Kinley.

Grandpa said, "But when Carl Ben heard about the Wright Brothers, I'll bet his interest just grew and grew. Ole used to read certain articles from the newspaper to the kids so they would know about interesting things going on in the world, and they would discuss them afterwards. I'm guessing that's how Carl Ben heard about the story of the Wright Brothers in the first place. Remember, this was even before radio and television existed."

"When did radio and television start again?" asked Thomas.

"Radio in North Dakota, about 1922, and television, about 1953," Grandpa answered. "But Carl Ben's interest in flying got even bigger when something pretty exciting came to their town of Hatton."

"What?" asked Thomas.

"A Chautauqua (shuh TAW kwuh)," replied Grandpa.

"What's a Chautauqua?" asked Kinley.

"Imagine a large group people coming to your town back in the late 1800s and early 1900s—up until about 1920. There were teachers and entertainers and preachers and showmen, plus other speakers that could talk about something of interest to people. They would come to town, set up in large tents or outside, and maybe for 25 cents or so, you could get in and enjoy all the things that the Chautauqua had to offer. After a few days, the Chautauqua would move on to another town."

"That sounds like fun," said Thomas.

"Yeah," said Kinley. "A little like a circus and a carnival put together without all the fancy rides."

"Where's the name *Chautauqua* come from?" asked Thomas.

"From Chautauqua Lake in New York, where the whole thing got started," Grandpa explained. "So, anyway, when Carl Ben found out there was going to be a flying machine at the Chautauqua, he got really excited. He went to the Chautauqua to see that flying machine, and he was a little disappointed when it turned out to be an invention that didn't work—one that looked a lot like a big kite. It was nothing like the Wright Brothers' plane. But the man who was speaking about that machine and flying said some things that were interesting to Carl Ben.

He learned about a man named George Pocock who actually designed a buggy that was pulled by a flying kite way back in 1822."

"No way!" said Thomas.

"Yes, I can show you a photo on my computer," said Grandpa.

Grandpa showed them the photo.

George Pocock and his kite; *Author's Collection*

"Wow!" Thomas exclaimed. "That's amazing!"

"How about this?" said Grandpa, showing them another photo. "Carl Ben learned about another guy from Germany named Otto Lilienthal, who built many gliders in the 1890s. I read that it was actually Otto's gliders that got the Wright Brothers really interested in flying."

"I'm not sure I'd try that," Kinley said, chuckling.

OTTO LILIENTHAL AND ONE OF HIS GLIDERS, *AUTHOR'S COLLECTION*

Grandpa said, "You can both imagine how excited Carl Ben must have been when he got home that day. For the next several days, he was reading and researching everything he could find about flying and flying machines, and then, you can probably guess what he did next."

"He tried to build his own?" Thomas guessed.

"That's exactly right, Thomas," said Grandpa. "He eventually sketched his plan, gathered materials together, got some help from his siblings and friends, and built a flying machine. I think it turned out to look more like a strange-looking kite."

"Did it fly?" asked Kinley.

"Yes, but with no passengers," answered Grandpa.

"I sure wish we had a photo of *that*," said Thomas.

CHAPTER 5

Two Hannahs

"Grandpa, would you please tell us about the two Hannahs now?" asked Kinley.

Grandpa said, "This is a sad part of the Carl Ben story, so you'd better get my box of Kleenex, just in case."

Thomas ran to Grandpa's office and got a box of Kleenex and placed it on the kitchen table.

"Thanks, Thomas," said Grandpa. "So, let's go back to 1908, when Carl Ben was 11, and he would have just finished the sixth grade. It was the summer, and a wonderful thing happened in the Eielson family. Twin girls were born. Their names were Helen and *Hannah*."

"That's Hannah number one," said Kinley.

"That's right," said Grandpa. "Everyone was happy, but Olava had a tough time getting her health back after giving birth. Elma, the oldest, was really great helping her mom with the twins and the other kids, which made a big difference. She also did a lot of the housework so her mother could get the extra rest she needed to get better. Mom got well again, but then, that winter, something awful happened."

"Please don't say Olava died," Thomas pleaded.

"No," Grandpa replied. "Actually, baby Hannah got really sick, and she died."

"Do you know what she died of?" Thomas asked sadly.

"No," replied Grandpa, "but you can imagine how difficult that was for the whole family—and it was extra tough on Olava. The kids loved their mother a lot, and they tried to think of ways they could cheer her up. Carl Ben wrote some funny plays about things like taking journeys to Alaska, searching for gold. Then he'd get some of his friends and his brothers and sisters to perform them for Olava. It really made her laugh."

"Did she get better?" asked Kinley.

"Yes," Grandpa replied, "Now, let's turn the clock ahead to the summer of 1910 when Carl Ben had finished the eighth grade. The family got some great news."

"Another baby!" Kinley said quickly.

"And they named her *Hannah*!" Thomas added.

"You two are way too smart," said Grandpa. "That's exactly right ... but I almost don't want to tell you what happened after that. Poor Olava had a really tough time after giving birth again, and then it just got worse. Olava got tuberculosis or TB."

"What's that?" asked Kinley.

Grandpa explained, "It's a disease that affects the lungs, and it's highly contagious. It used to be called *consumption* because of the weight loss associated with it. It involves a real nasty cough too. Thank goodness they found out how to prevent it and treat it with antibiotics back in the 1940s and '50s so you don't have to worry about it."

"But what about Olava?" asked Kinley, dreading what Grandpa was going to say next.

"Back when Olava got tuberculosis, they sent people to places called sanitariums. They were places where people got bed rest and clean air, but patients were isolated from others because the disease was so contagious. So Olava was away from the family for a long time, and only Ole could visit her because of how contagious TB was, and he was away from the family a lot during this time. … Anyway, the next year, just three days after Carl Ben's fourteenth birthday, Olava died."

"That's so sad," said Kinley, taking a Kleenex.

"You can imagine how tough that must have been," Grandpa continued, "Olava was just a little over 40, the mother of all those kids and still so young, and baby Hannah was only about nine months old. The whole family must have been just devastated."

"I'm so glad they had each other, plus their faith in God to help them through," said Thomas.

"That's so true," said Grandpa. "Carl Ben had a pretty tough time with it. Here he was—about ready to become a freshman in high school, and the mother he loved so much was not around anymore. But Carl Ben remembered his mom's words and they motivated him. She always told him, 'Be sure to finish high school and go to college so you can continue to develop your thinking and reasoning.' And Carl Ben wasn't going to let her down."

"I can't even imagine," said Kinley, wiping tears from her eyes.

"Carl Ben became more serious, and he felt pretty lonely without his mom around," said Grandpa. "Elma was so great, because she did a lot of the things her mother did to keep the family together. But now Carl Ben had to go through high school without his wonderful mother."

"How did that go?" asked Thomas.

"Pretty good, I think," said Grandpa. "I think their memories of their wonderful mother encouraged Carl Ben and the rest of the family as they were living their lives. Carl Ben excelled in high school, and he worked a lot at his dad's store too. Besides his schoolwork, Carl Ben was really good at basketball and debate."

"You were in debate, weren't you, Grandpa?" asked Kinley. "What is it again?"

Grandpa smiled. "To be honest, debate might have been the best thing I did in high school because it helped me so much in life. It helps you think on your feet, and getting up in a front of a crowd is easy after you've debated for a while. Debate is a lot like an organized argument, where you have a specific topic, and you present your best argument on one side or the other. Then someone presents the other side of the argument, and after that, you have a chance go back at each other's arguments again."

"Could you give us an example of something Carl Ben might have debated?" asked Thomas.

"Okay," said Grandpa, "here's an actual topic that Carl Ben debated, and you can bet he spent a great deal of time developing his argument because it was so important to him. The argument involved this issue: *Airplanes are the best means of transportation for the future.* In debate someone takes the affirmative side supporting that view, and someone takes the negative side against that view. Carl Ben had to develop a good case for aviation becoming the best mode of transportation. Try to guess some of the reasons he came up with when he was developing his argument."

"You can travel faster and save time?" Kinley guessed.

Thomas tried. "You can get to places that are out of the way?" he said.

"Yes," said Grandpa, "Carl Ben loved debating and he was good at it, but he practiced in a way much different than I ever did."

"What do you mean?" asked Thomas.

Grandpa chuckled. "He used to practice his arguments while he was milking the family cow, Clara Belle. In fact, Carl Ben gave Clara Belle a lot of credit for his debating ability."

Kinley and Thomas laughed.

"Cows can be *awesome* listeners," Kinley said, still laughing.

Grandpa said, "And Carl Ben graduated from Hatton High School in the spring of 1914. There were four boys and five girls in his graduating class."

"How big was your graduating class at Mandan High School?" asked Thomas.

"Two hundred seventy-six," answered Grandpa. "For Carl Ben, he would soon be off to college at the University of North Dakota."

Kinley said, "His mother sure would have been proud of him."

"No doubt," said Grandpa.

CHAPTER 6

College

"Carl Ben was a little anxious before he went off to UND," Grandpa explained. "He really wasn't sure what he wanted to study there."

"Grandpa?" said Thomas. "Didn't your friend Dominic Feeney learn how to fly planes at the University of North Dakota?"

"Yes, he did," Grandpa said, smiling, "but UND's Aviation School didn't get going until 1968, and Carl Ben was there in 1914, when aviation was still a pretty new thing. By the way, I looked that up. UND's Department of Aviation began in 1968 with two donated planes and twelve students, but it has now become an important department on campus. But, of course, Carl Ben didn't have aviation as an option back then. But he did have two other options on his mind for college. Option number one: he could study business because his dad wanted Carl Ben to eventually take over the store in Hatton with his brother Edwin. Option number two: he could study the law. His high school teachers saw his potential to be a great lawyer or politician because of his exceptional ability as a thinker, speaker, and debater, and they had encouraged him to study law."

"Which one did he choose?" asked Thomas.

"He chose business, and after he made that choice, Ole told Carl Ben he would support him if he ever changed his mind."

"And he did, didn't he?" said Kinley.

"Yes, he did," Grandpa replied. "And it didn't take long, as you'll soon find out. ... Anyway, when Carl Ben left for college, it was his first time away from home for more than a couple of days, so you can imagine how he felt."

"Yeah," said Thomas, "but he was only about 40 miles from home, so he could go home on the weekends if he got homesick and stuff."

"That's true, but it was still a big step," said Grandpa. "Ole actually let Carl Ben take the family's Cadillac when he took off for UND that first time. You can imagine Carl Ben's family and friends saying goodbye as he left for Grand Forks."

"What did a Cadillac look like back then?" asked Thomas.

"Why don't you find one for me on my computer," Grandpa said.

Thomas found a photo of a 1914 Cadillac.

"Pretty cool," said Thomas.

"I'd ride in that in the Mandan Parade," said Kinley.

"And I would be your driver in the parade," said Grandpa, with a chuckle.

"Did Carl Ben like college?" asked Thomas.

1914 Cadillac; *Author's Collection*

"He was homesick and missed his family a lot at first," Grandpa answered. "But then he got into his schedule of classes and other activities and it got better."

"What kind of activities?" Kinley wanted to know.

Grandpa said, "He got into debate, he played cornet in the band, he joined a fraternity and played basketball for their team, and he was even in the glee club."

"What's a glee club?" asked Thomas.

"It's a singing group or choir," Grandpa answered.

"Did he have a girlfriend?" asked Kinley.

"No," said Grandpa, chuckling, "but his sister Elma teased him about that. Carl Ben told her he didn't want to get too serious about girls until he was ready to settle down."

"Smart man," said Thomas, giggling.

Grandpa continued, "When he was a sophomore,

some of the law professors started to recognize Carl Ben's potential to become a good lawyer, and he decided to change his focus. Then he transferred to the University of Wisconsin to pursue his interest in law. But he only lasted a semester there when something happened."

"I know he didn't flunk out of school. What happened?" Kinley asked.

"The First World War got Carl Ben's attention, and he wanted to do his part in our country's fight against Germany."

"Teddy Roosevelt wasn't still president, was he?" asked Thomas.

"No," Grandpa answered. "The president was Woodrow Wilson, who Teddy had recently lost to when he tried to run for a third presidential term."

"Did Carl Ben know a lot about Teddy?" asked Kinley.

"Carl Ben thought the world of Teddy," said Grandpa. "After all, Teddy was the first president to ever fly in an airplane."

"Really!?" Thomas exclaimed. "When did he do that?"

"He flew at a flying exhibition on October 11, 1910, in St. Louis, when Carl Ben would have been 13. Carl Ben kept the newspaper clippings from that event in his scrapbook. Believe it or not, Teddy flew in a Wright Brothers plane piloted by a guy name Archie Hoxsey. I think I can find a photo of that event."

Grandpa found a photo on his computer and showed them.

"No way!" said Kinley.

"Pretty cool, huh?" said Grandpa.

Teddy's flight; *Author's Collection*

"Did Teddy have fun?" asked Thomas.

Grandpa chuckled. "At first, even Teddy turned down Hoxsey's invitation to fly, but then he changed his mind and went on a short flight that lasted about four minutes, and it included three steep dives. He loved it! He thought it was the best experience he'd ever had. You know what he used to say when he really liked something, don't you?"

"BULLY!" Kinley and Thomas said at the same time.

Kinley asked, "Do you know whatever happened to Archie Hoxsey?"

Grandpa was quiet for a second or two.

"He crashed, didn't he?" Kinley said, bracing herself.

"Unfortunately, he did," said Grandpa. "Just a few months after taking Teddy for that ride, Archie set an altitude record by flying up to more than 11,000 feet in the air, but then he died the next day in a crash."

"Yikes!" Thomas exclaimed.

"That's for sure," said Grandpa. "Those early fliers had to have lot of guts. … By the way, I'm not sure if Carl Ben ever met Teddy, but I have a feeling Carl Ben knew much more about Teddy than that story about the first flight. Carl Ben loved stories of adventure, and Teddy's life was loaded with adventure."

Kinley said, "You mean like all that stuff you told us about Teddy before—like when he came to North Dakota the first time to hunt buffalo in 1883, and then he returned a year later after both his mother and wife died on Valentine's Day."

Thomas continued, "Then he got toughened up by the cowboy life in North Dakota, became a hero of the Spanish-American War when he charged up San Juan Hill, and that led to him becoming president."

Grandpa looked at Kinley and Thomas. "Sometimes, you two *amaze* me!"

"We haven't even mentioned all the other stuff you told us like his trip to the Amazon jungle where he almost died," said Kinley.

Grandpa smiled. "I've got another Teddy story that's hard to believe that took place at about the same time Carl Ben was deciding to leave school to fight in World War I. Believe it or not, Teddy, who was about 58 at the time and a former president, was forming a volunteer group of soldiers to fight in that war. Many of them were the same Roughriders he had fought with 19 years earlier in the Spanish-American War."

"Did Teddy do it?" asked Thomas.

"No, President Wilson didn't allow him to do it," said Grandpa. "I think Wilson thought Teddy would become such a hero that he'd run for president again and beat him. But Teddy's sons all fought in the war, and they paid a heavy price. Quentin was a pilot, and he was killed when his plane was shot down. Archie and Ted were wounded in battle, and Kermit fought bravely but wasn't wounded."

Kinley asked, "What happened to Carl Ben during World War I?"

"I'll get to that next," said Grandpa.

Carl Ben in uniform; *State Historical Society of North Dakota*

CHAPTER 7

Carl Ben the Cadet

Grandpa said, "Carl Ben and many of his classmates at the University of Wisconsin were paying attention to what was going on with the war in Europe. I think they realized that the United States wasn't going to be able to stay out of the war much longer. Some events were happening that were getting us closer to getting into the fight."

"What kind of events?" asked Thomas.

"A big one was the sinking of a huge passenger ship called the *Lusitania*. I've got a photo of that here somewhere."

Grandpa showed them the photo.

"What happened, Grandpa?" Kinley wanted to know.

"A German U-boat or submarine torpedoed the large passenger ship, and 1,198 passengers were killed, including 128 Americans."

"That's awful!" exclaimed Kinley.

The Lusitania sinking; *Author's Collection*

"Why were they called U-boats?" asked Thomas.

"The 'U' is an abbreviation for the German word *Unterseeboot*, which means *undersea boat*. ... So, anyway, as many of Carl Ben's classmates started to see that war was probably inevitable, they began to leave school and volunteer for the infantry, and Carl Ben thought about doing the same thing."

"What's *infantry*, Grandpa?" asked Kinley.

"It's basically foot soldiers," Grandpa replied.

"But Carl Ben loved flying, so he joined the Air Force?" Thomas guessed.

"Close," said Grandpa. "There really wasn't a United States Air Force until 1947. But there was something like it back then called the U.S. Signal Corps, Aviation Section, which was a forerunner of the Air Force, and Carl Ben enlisted on January 17, 1917, even before our country declared war on Germany on April 6. ... And that day was a huge day in Carl Ben's life because after that day, flying became the most important focus in his life."

"What kinds of planes did he learn to fly?" Kinley asked.

"I've got a few photos to show you. Carl Ben learned how to fly with the Curtiss JN-4, called the *Jenny*."

Grandpa showed them two photos.

Jenny JN-4 airplane; *Author's Collection*

"I'm not sure I'd fly in one of those," said Kinley.

"I would," said Thomas.

"I'd fly if Carl Ben was the pilot," said Grandpa. "The aircraft were built by the Curtiss Aeroplane Company in the state of New York. Keep in mind, this wasn't that long after Kitty Hawk in 1903, so the aircraft were pretty basic and really dangerous to fly, but there were lots of brave men who volunteered to fly them for our country. Unfortunately, after Carl Ben completed his ground training and was just beginning to learn how to fly in California, another tragedy happened in his family."

"Oh no, Grandpa!" said Kinley. "Now what?"

"Edwin died of tuberculosis," said Grandpa.

"The same disease his mother died of," said Kinley.

"And you can imagine how sad everyone in the family felt," said Grandpa. "After the funeral, Oliver and Arthur took over the duties at the store in Hatton, and Carl Ben went back to California to continue his flight training feeling really sad. Then he took his first solo flight, and that was it. It was the best thing to help lift him out his deep sadness. He knew that he would never give up flying in his life no matter what."

"Was Carl Ben a good pilot?" asked Thomas.

"He became a really good pilot, but I read a few stories about him getting lost during his training. It wasn't an uncommon thing back then, though. Just imagine flying through the air in an open cockpit airplane with very few instruments to help with navigation, with clouds and other things making it hard to see the ground. Maybe you're holding a map in your hand and glancing at it as you're flying."

"I'm already lost," said Kinley.

"Me too," said Grandpa, chuckling. "Some pilots back then used to land and ask for directions, or they might have flown over the railroad tracks to a railroad station, hoping to see the station name somewhere on the depot or platform so they would know where they were. Anyway, Carl Ben eventually earned his second lieutenant's commission, and then he received orders to go to France after Christmas and join the war effort. But then something pretty amazing happened."

"What?" Kinley asked.

"Well," said Grandpa, "as he was waiting to leave for France, he and his fellow fliers did a lot of extra training, flying cross-country and learning some aerobatic flying tactics."

"What are aerobatic flying tactics?" asked Thomas.

"Those were the different maneuvers and stunts that helped a pilot get an advantage when he was in a fight against another plane. … So, anyway, that amazing thing happened when Carl Ben was coming back from one of these training sessions before he was to leave for France. On November 11, 1918, he was returning from one of his training missions, and he noticed a bunch of people dancing down on the runway below."

"The war was over!" Thomas guessed.

"You're way too smart," said Grandpa. "And November 11 just happens to be—"

"Veterans Day!" Kinley exclaimed.

"How did Carl Ben feel?" asked Thomas.

Grandpa said, "On the one hand, you can imagine how everyone felt about the war being over—extremely happy that there would be no more war. On the other hand, Carl Ben and many of his friends had trained a long time for one purpose, and now that was over. But it had been over two years since Carl Ben enlisted, and now he was a trained flier, and he knew that's what he wanted to do the rest of his life. Many people still thought flying was never really going to become an important part of people's lives, but Carl Ben knew better. He was determined to become part of America's flying future."

CHAPTER 8

Back Home in Hatton

"Do you two wanna guess what Carl Ben does as soon as he gets back to Hatton?" asked Grandpa.

"He buys an airplane and starts the world's first airline," Thomas said quickly.

"Kinley?"

Kinley took a deep breath, and then she got a funny look on her face. "I'll go along with the buying the airplane—but then I'm guessing he takes that airplane and flies back to college, and there he meets a lovely girl named Bonnie, who just happens to be the homecoming queen and captain of the basketball team. They go to the homecoming dance together, and afterward, they fly together all over the state in their free time until they graduate from college. After that, they get married and have nine children."

Grandpa and Thomas gave Kinley a funny look, then all three of them burst out laughing.

"Wow!" said Grandpa, still laughing. "That's an amazing story, Kinley!"

"Thanks," said Kinley, chuckling. "Did I get anything right?"

"Actually, you *did*," said Grandpa. "Here's what *really* happened when he got back to Hatton. You can imagine how great it was for Carl Ben to come home with the war over and everything. Adeline said it was even better than Christmas. Carl Ben was happy to be home, working at the Hatton Farmers' Mercantile Store, and he took advantage of every opportunity he could to promote aviation to anyone who would listen to him. It didn't take long for him to find out that most of the people in Hatton felt the same way as his dad about flying. Most thought flying was just a fad, and it was way too dangerous. It would never catch on. But Carl Ben didn't let that bother him. He just kept on promoting the thing he loved."

"Those debating skills helped him, didn't they?" said Thomas.

"That's for sure," said Grandpa. "Carl Ben emphasized how profitable airplanes would be in the future as a means of transportation. They could help agriculture by spraying for grasshoppers and other insects and for delivery of mail and other things. It didn't take long, and Carl Ben got enough people in Hatton to start the first flying club in North Dakota and one of the first in the whole country—the Hatton Aero Club."

"What's *aero* mean?" asked Thomas.

"It's short for *aeronautical*," Grandpa replied. "It involves the science of designing, building, and flying aircraft."

"How many were in the Aero Club?" asked Kinley.

"Nine, I think," Grandpa answered.

"I'll bet his dad didn't join the club," said Kinley.

"You're absolutely right," said Grandpa. "Actually, many of the first members of the flying club were lifelong friends of Carl Ben. By early 1920, the club got enough money together to make a down payment of $265 on a Jenny that cost about $2,500."

"My prediction about getting the plane was right!" exclaimed Thomas.

"Mine too!" said Kinley.

"How did they pay for the airplane?" asked Thomas.

Grandpa explained, "They printed up a brochure to advertise their money-making ideas. A big part of that next summer involved Carl Ben traveling to towns and performing flying stunts for crowds at local fairs for about $200 per day."

"What kind of stunts?" asked Thomas.

"I've got the names for the ones they advertised. There were tail slides, tail spins, loops, wing overs, barrel rolls, power spirals, Immelman turns, the falling leaf, side slips, and the vertical virage. These were flying maneuvers that Carl Ben had learned to perform in case he was involved in any dogfights or aerial battles with enemy aircraft during the war."

"Could you show us some of them?" asked Kinley.

"We can do that later," said Grandpa. "I know you've seen some of them at the big air shows we've gone to. Maybe we can take one of my old model airplanes outside and demonstrate them later."

"Awesome!" said Thomas.

"What did Ole say about all of this Aero Club business?" asked Kinley.

"He definitely wasn't thrilled about any of it," said

Grandpa. "Ole and Carl Ben had a little talk, and Carl Ben promised he would go back to school even if things worked out with the flying club."

"Did they work out?" Kinley asked.

"I'm not going to jump ahead," said Grandpa. "There's so much I like about this part of the story. Just imagine this. They had just purchased the Jenny, and now Carl Ben flies it back to Hatton from Minneapolis."

"Was anyone flying with him?" Kinley wanted to know.

"Yes," replied Grandpa, "a farmer named Thorval Stavens, who was also the secretary-treasurer of the flying club. He was flying in the open cockpit behind Carl Ben, wearing googles and a helmet. ... It must have been unbelievably exciting to have been in Hatton that day as the plane approached the town. Many people were seeing an airplane for the first time ever. People rushed out of stores and other places in Hatton as they heard and saw the plane approaching. Ole followed the people who rushed out of his store onto Main Street, and you can only imagine how *he* felt. And Carl Ben made sure it would be an event that no one would ever forget. He said later that he had as much fun that day as he ever had—as much fun as when he took his first solo flight. He put on a little acrobatic show for the townspeople, and when he was done, he slowly circled the town several times and took it all in, enjoying every moment."

"I wish I could have been there to see that," said Thomas.

"Me too," said Kinley.

"Me three," said Grandpa. "And when he landed, he was greeted with lots of cheering. Some club members lifted Carl Ben and Thorval Stavens on their shoulders. There was more cheering from the crowd as they escorted the two men into a convertible, and they started driving around town. Other cars got behind them, honking their horns, and it didn't take long before a parade of cars was honking and celebrating this super-special event."

"That is so cool!" said Kinley.

"And it got even better," said Grandpa. "That Sunday after church, the flying club put on their first public event, a free show for the town of Hatton. Pretty much the whole town of Hatton gathered at the ballpark in town to watch that performance, and it was a great one. Carl Ben put on a show with a bunch of awesome stunts, some he had never even tried before."

"Did his dad show up?" asked Thomas.

"Yes, and you can imagine how nervous he was," said Grandpa. "After it was all over, Ole and Carl Ben talked, and at one point Carl Ben offered to take his dad up for a ride. Guess what Ole said."

"No way!" Kinley guessed.

"That's right," said Grandpa, chuckling.

CHAPTER 9

The Summer Flies By

"How did the summer go?" asked Kinley.

"It was anything but boring," said Grandpa. "Carl Ben and Garv Olson, who was one of Carl Ben's boyhood friends, flew to lots of towns, and they performed stunts for that $200 a day I told you about before. When he had time, Carl Ben also took people on rides for about 15 dollars or so, depending on the length of the flight.

"Ole wasn't at all thrilled with the whole thing, but Carl Ben promised his dad he was going back to college at the University of North Dakota at the end of the summer. However, Carl Ben also told his dad he wasn't going to ever give up on his dream of helping make flying an important part of America's future. He let his dad know that the stunt flying was a good way to get people more interested in flying, but he definitely didn't want to do it forever."

"Did Carl Ben get people interested?" asked Thomas.

"In a big way," Grandpa answered. "His flying

exhibitions just got better and more thrilling as the summer went on. Carl Ben performed his stunts at altitudes up to 10,000 feet, which no one else did at the time, and more and more people started to hear about Carl Ben and his amazing flying. He even had fans that followed him from town to town."

"Groupies," said Thomas, giggling.

"I guess so," said Grandpa with a chuckle. "Carl Ben's flying antics were making the newspapers quite a bit, and even Ole seemed pretty happy when he got newspaper clippings from his friends. He had some of his children put them in a scrapbook."

"He must have been proud, even though he was afraid," said Kinley.

"I think that's right," said Grandpa. "And Ole must have approved when something else happened that summer. Carl Ben had what was called his first commercial flight, and I think his dad liked that a lot."

"What's a commercial flight?" asked Thomas.

"Commerce involves business, and Carl Ben was hired to deliver a large amount of money from Walhalla, North Dakota, to Morden, Manitoba, about 25 miles away. It was pretty awesome, because Carl Ben even landed the plane at night with 25 automobiles lighting up the landing area with their headlights."

"Cool," said Thomas. "Do you have any idea how *Walhalla* got its name?"

"Yes," Grandpa answered. "I had to look that up because it's such a funny name. *Walhalla* sounds a lot like *Valhalla*, the home of the gods in Norse mythology. It turns out someone thought the area around there in North Dakota was so beautiful that it reminded them of

Valhalla, and *Walhalla* is just a version of that name."

"I like it," said Thomas.

"Me too," said Kinley.

Grandpa said, "I've got to tell you about Carl Ben's first flying exhibition in Minnesota, in a town named Elbow Lake, because it's a good example of how Carl Ben and Garv decided to use flying for a really good purpose. While they were in Elbow Lake, they found out that a nurse living there named Ella Ness was a missionary, and she would soon be going to Madagascar, a country in East Africa. Ella needed money to buy some of the supplies she would need to help the people there. Carl Ben and Garv decided they would give Ella two-thirds of the money they earned for the flights that Carl Ben took passengers on right after their stunt flying exhibition."

"How much did they earn for Ella?" asked Kinley.

"About $250—which went a long way back then," said Grandpa. "It bought lots of supplies, and Ella was extremely happy and thankful. Carl Ben even took her on a free ride, which she really liked, although she was a little afraid at the start."

"I would have been too," said Kinley. "Especially in those old planes."

Thomas asked, "Did Carl Ben have any accidents that summer?"

Grandpa grimaced. "You can imagine there were some problems. Landing an airplane is such a critical thing, and Carl Ben didn't always have the best landing areas for his plane that summer. Also, remember, those early planes weren't very advanced so there were quite a few engine problems—and when you have engine troubles up in the air, you know what that means."

"Emergency landing," said Thomas.

"And that meant Carl Ben and Garv had to find a suitable place to land very quickly, and it must have been pretty hard at times with all the holes and rocks and stuff that could cause some real problems. But Carl Ben and Garv did an amazing job under pressure *most* of the time. … But it got really interesting one time toward the end of the summer when they went to Glenwood, Minnesota, and the small landing area for their plane was pretty awful after a bunch of rain had fallen earlier."

"They got stuck in the mud?" Kinley guessed.

"You got it," said Grandpa, "but it was even more precarious than that. Not only were they stuck in the mud, but if they were to ever get out, they had just a small area to fly out of, with a grandstand on one side and large cottonwood trees on the other three sides."

"Not good at all," said Thomas. "What did they do?"

"It was a real puzzler," said Grandpa. "Carl Ben even walked in his sleep trying to figure out what they could do. On the third day, he thought he had a solution. Garv stayed on the ground, and they drained almost all the fuel out, leaving just enough to maybe get the plane off the ground and fly to solid ground nearby to refuel. Then Carl Ben went full throttle, and a bunch of volunteers lifted and pushed the plane to help get it moving. Amazingly, Carl Ben was able to get the plane off the ground and into the air. Then, he just *barely* made it over the cottonwoods. Picture the wings of Carl Ben's plane swishing over the tops of the trees, then the tail of the plane catches on a tree branch and carries it away."

"Wow!" Thomas exclaimed. "Close call!"

"Yes, it was," said Grandpa. "A close call, but he made it. Then he landed nearby, fueled up, and picked up Garv before taking off for the next town."

"Pretty amazing," said Kinley.

Grandpa said, "This doesn't involve an accident or anything, but at the end of July, something pretty interesting happened in Portal, North Dakota, that might give you two a little hint of Carl Ben's future."

"Where does *Portal* get its name?" asked Kinley.

"It's on the border between Canada and the United States, so it's a *port* of entry. … So anyway, on this day in late July, Carl Ben and Garv were in Portal when four DH-4 De Havilland planes that were part of a special group called the Black Wolf Squadron came flying in formation into the town of Portal."

"What were they doing?" asked Thomas.

"Those four planes were actually on an amazing journey—flying all the way from New York City to Nome, Alaska. Carl Ben knew they were going to be in Portal that day, but Garv didn't, so it was quite a surprise for him."

Kinley asked, "Where did they get the name *Black Wolf Squadron*?"

"Their official name was the Alaskan Flying Expedition," said Grandpa. "But there was a black wolf painted on the side of each of the planes, so they became known as the Black Wolf Squadron."

"Why were they flying to Alaska?" asked Kinley.

"There was a general named Billy Mitchell who wanted to prove that airplanes could be an important part of our country's defense—that flying long distances, even to Alaska, was possible."

"Did they make it all the way to Nome?" asked Thomas.

Black Wolf Squadron pilots and plane; *Author's Collection*

"Yes," Grandpa replied. "They left New York on July 15 and made it to Nome, Alaska, on August 24."

"Why did it take them more than a month?" asked Thomas.

Grandpa explained, "There was the weather, frequent stops for fuel, and making sure the landing places along the way were safe. Remember, there were no airports and stuff back then. The flying time was only about 50 hours for the 4,500 miles they flew, but that was still quick compared to the people that made that trip during the gold rush days in Alaska. Back then, it took about 20 months to make the trek."

"Wow!" Thomas exclaimed.

"It's pretty amusing," said Grandpa, "when they got to Juneau, one of the Black Wolf Squadron pilots dropped a *New York Times* newspaper out of his plane for the governor of Alaska. This was way before Alaska became a state so he would have been the territorial governor.

Anyway, the newspaper landed on the top of a hotel, and I guess they called it the first air mail to arrive in Alaska."

"Too funny," said Kinley.

"I forgot to mention something," said Grandpa. "It was pretty cool because Carl Ben and Garv got to help the Black Wolf Squadron out when they were in Portal. One of the pilots had a damaged plane, and Carl Ben and Garv managed to help fix it for them."

"Grandpa?" said Kinley. "Why should this part of Carl Ben's story give us a hint of Carl Ben's future?"

"Why don't you guess," said Grandpa.

CHAPTER 10

Climax, Minnesota

"I'm not sure you even want to hear about how the summer flying exhibitions ended that summer," said Grandpa.

"Oh no!" said Kinley. "Just tell me Carl Ben wasn't hurt."

"He luckily wasn't hurt, but you won't believe what happened," said Grandpa. "It was late August, and things had gone pretty well all summer for Carl Ben and Garv. They were making good money and saving hotel bills by sleeping under the plane at night almost all the time. They flew to the town of Climax, Minnesota, where they were going to perform flying stunts, and once again, they landed in the area that the townspeople had prepared for them. But right after they landed, Carl Ben realized they were in a dangerous place."

"Why?" asked Thomas.

"The field was muddy, but that was just the beginning. When Carl Ben looked at the area they would need to take off from, it wasn't safe at all."

"What was wrong with it?" Thomas asked.

"It was a small area with lots of tall elm trees around it, plus at the end of the strip of land where the plane would lift off, there were railroad tracks running perpendicular to it with telephone lines running along the tracks on both sides. So, Carl Ben decided that he needed to try to get to a safer place that he had spotted while flying into the town—and he needed to do it right away. He told Garv to stay out of the plane just in case something bad happened. Then Carl Ben prepared to take off."

"Oh no!" exclaimed Kinley. "The plane hits the wires, doesn't it?"

"It hits a pole?" Thomas guessed.

"Unfortunately, you're both *kinda* right," said Grandpa. "First, some mud got stuck in the wheels, and that kept the plane from taking off as soon as it should have, and Carl Ben knew he was in trouble right away. He also knew he wasn't going to fly above the telephone poles and telephone lines. He had to try to fly under the first set of wires and over the second set—but it didn't work. He made it under the first set of wires and flew over the railroad tracks. But then one of the wings of the plane hit a telephone pole, and the plane wrapped around it and crashed to the ground."

"But Carl Ben wasn't hurt!?" asked Kinley, cringing.

"No, surprisingly not," Grandpa answered. "Garv ran over and was relieved that Carl Ben was okay, but the plane was a mess. The landing gear and one of the wings were destroyed."

"I'll bet Ole wasn't too thrilled when he heard about

it," said Thomas.

"He was definitely upset," said Grandpa, "but I guess he also said that at least he would have one night where he didn't have to worry about Carl Ben flying—because Carl Ben *couldn't* fly in what was left of the plane. Oliver and Arthur brought a truck and picked up the wrecked plane. The wreckage was put in the Eielsons' backyard. The engine was sold to some guy for $200. He was going to use it on his boat, I guess. The flying club in Hatton was done, and Carl Ben bought the wreckage without the motor and moved it to a barn near their house, where he was determined to get it working again."

"Did he do it?" asked Kinley.

"He sure did," answered Grandpa. "He even flew it to UND for college when school started in the fall."

"No way!" said Thomas. "I'll bet he was the first person to fly to college in North Dakota."

"I'll bet you're right," said Grandpa.

"How did things go for him in college?" Kinley asked.

"Pretty good, I think," replied Grandpa, "but it couldn't have been easy going back to school after the war and after the exciting summer he'd just had. Thankfully, there were plenty of other World War I veterans on the UND campus, plus Oliver was starting school there as a freshman. Carl Ben became good friends with two flyers named Frank Talcott and Speed Holman, and those three had lots of flying experiences to share. They even did some stunt flying that fall before it got really cold outside."

"Did anything interesting happen that year at UND?" asked Kinley.

"You'll like this, Kinley," said Grandpa. "Carl Ben dated quite a few girls that year at UND, and he even flew to Wisconsin to pick up a girl he had met when he went to school there. Then he took her to the Halloween Ball at UND and flew her back to Wisconsin afterward."

"That's awesome," said Kinley.

Grandpa said, "Another time, Carl Ben flew to some farmer's place to set up some business for the next summer, when something pretty strange happened."

"What?" asked Thomas.

"Take a guess," said Grandpa.

Thomas smiled. "A pack of angry chickens attacked the plane," he guessed.

Grandpa looked at Kinley. "I'm guessing a big bull charged at the plane," she said.

Grandpa chuckled. "Both guesses are pretty good," he said, "but you got the kind of animals wrong. Actually, some sheep ate part of one of the wings of the plane, but Carl Ben was able to fly it anyway, even though he said it was a little rough going."

Kinley and Thomas laughed.

Grandpa said, "Carl Ben only had one year left to finish his bachelor's degree, and he got his diploma in June of 1921. After that, he had plans to go to law school at Georgetown in Washington, D.C., but not until he had another summer of stunt flying."

"How did that go?" asked Kinley. "No accidents, I hope."

"It went really well, and he had no accidents that I know of," said Grandpa. "He and his two flying friends from UND were really busy that whole summer, but they also had lots of fun. One thing that happened is definitely worth mentioning because it was pretty unbelievable. They went to a town to perform stunts, and there was another group of men who was supposed to be performing flying stunts after them. As it turned out, though, the first day the second group got into town, their plane wasn't working. They had heard what a great pilot Carl Ben was, so they asked him if he would fly his plane for their act. Carl Ben thought it would be impossible to learn the act so quickly and then not practice it at all, but he listened to what they had in mind, and he agreed to do it."

"Was it pretty crazy?" asked Kinley.

"That's a good way to describe it," said Grandpa. "Here's what the trickiest part of the whole act involved. One guy, I'll call Thomas, would be driving a car at a pretty good speed. Another guy, I'll call him Myron, would be sitting on the end of one of the wings of Carl Ben's plane. So, picture this. Carl Ben does a few loops with the guy sitting on the plane's wing—then he flies over the car going at a good speed—then the guy on the wing drops a rope ladder down from the wing and climbs down onto the top of the car. I've got a photo of a stunt like that, only there's a boat involved instead of a car."

Grandpa showed them the photo.

"No way I'd do that!" said Thomas. "Did Myron and Carl Ben and Thomas do it okay?"

"Yes, they do, but that's not the end of the stunt," said Grandpa. "Eventually, Carl Ben flies back and picks Myron up off the roof of the car."

"Did it all work?" asked Kinley.

"Yes, it did," said Grandpa, "Unfortunately, though, it didn't work so well the next day when the regular pilot was back flying his own plane that had been repaired. Carl Ben and his friends ended up visiting Myron in the hospital."

FLYING STUNT; *AUTHOR'S COLLECTION*

CHAPTER 11

Washington, D.C.

"Carl Ben was really excited to get to Washington, D.C., in the fall of 1921," said Grandpa.

"Who was the president in 1921?" Thomas asked.

"Warren Harding," Grandpa answered. "He had only been president for a short time when Carl Ben got to Washington."

"Was Teddy Roosevelt still alive?" asked Thomas.

"Teddy died on January 6, 1919, about three years before Carl Ben got to Washington. But, as you know, Carl Ben had read a lot about Teddy, and you can bet all that reading just added to his excitement about being in our nation's capital. Not long after Carl Ben arrived there, he went to the office of North Dakota's congressman named Olger Burtness, and Burtness helped Carl Ben get a part-time job with the Capitol Police Force working as a guard at the House of Representatives Office Building. Carl Ben loved the job because he got to meet a lot of interesting people from all over the world. One of the people he met was a delegate to Congress from Alaska named Dan Sutherland."

"There's *Alaska* again," Thomas noted.

"Yeah," said Kinley. "But how could Sutherland be in Congress if Alaska wasn't even a state yet? We learned in school that Alaska became a state in 1959."

"You're so smart, Kinley," said Grandpa, smiling. "We bought Alaska from the Russians way back in 1867 for two cents an acre, but it wouldn't become a state until 1959. So, Dan Sutherland was not a regular member of Congress. He was a *nonvoting delegate*. There are some nonvoting delegates in Congress right now—for territories of the United States like the U.S. Virgin Islands, for example. I think if they're not elected from one of the states, they can vote in the committees they're on, but not vote on final laws and stuff. ... Anyway, Sutherland and Carl Ben became friends right away, especially with Carl Ben's strong interest in Alaska. The two discussed lots of things about Alaska, including the Black Wolf Squadron's flight there, the amazing beauty of the place, and the need for air mail there because of the huge distances between towns and the rough terrain."

"I'm getting a strong feeling Carl Ben moves to Alaska," said Kinley.

"You're right again," said Grandpa. "After spending a lot of time talking with Sutherland, suddenly Alaska became more important in Carl Ben's mind than law school. Then, one day, Sutherland told Carl Ben about a job opening in the high school in Fairbanks, Alaska, that began the next fall. If he took the job, Carl Ben would have to teach science, English, and coach basketball, and I guess he would have to supervise some other sports too."

"And he takes the job?" Thomas guessed.

"Yes, he does," said Grandpa. "He finishes his first year of law school at Georgetown then he goes home to Hatton for the summer before heading to Alaska."

"How did he get to Alaska?" asked Thomas.

"It certainly wasn't easy back in 1922," said Grandpa. "He took the train to Seattle, then he boarded a steamer ship called the *Northwestern* that took him to Seward, Alaska. After that, he got on a train that took him almost all the way to Fairbanks."

The steamer *Northwestern*: *Author's Collection*

"How far was that from North Dakota?" asked Kinley.

Grandpa said, "We can figure it out later, but I estimate it to be about 3,000 miles. It must have been an incredible trip for Carl Ben, seeing land so much different than the prairies of North Dakota that he had grown up on—traveling to a land with unbelievable beauty that he'd read so much about."

"What a dream come true!" said Thomas.

"It certainly was," said Grandpa. "But there was something else that made that trip so special. From Seattle to Fairbanks, he made friends with an old-timer from Alaska—they called the old-timers *sourdoughs*. People like Carl Ben who were new to Alaska were called *cheechakos*. Anyway, this sourdough had come to Alaska about 20 years earlier to look for gold, and he knew a lot about the huge territory. You can imagine how many questions Carl Ben had for this sourdough and all the things the two men discussed. The old man was skeptical about the use of planes in Alaska, but Carl Ben didn't give up trying to convince him otherwise. They get to Fairbanks, and Carl Ben describes it as having wonderful people, about 3,000 of them. It had mostly small log houses, with two lousy roads leaving town, one going to Chatanika and the other to Valdez. Prices were much higher than North Dakota."

"Where did Carl Ben stay?" asked Kinley.

"He stayed at the Hotel Alaska," Grandpa answered. "He also had a roommate, so it must have been a little like his living in the dorm in college."

"How big is Fairbanks now?" asked Thomas.

"It has about 32,000 people now," Grandpa answered.

CHAPTER 12

Teaching in Fairbanks

Kinley said, "I'll bet it didn't take long before Carl Ben flew his first plane in Alaska."

Grandpa smiled. "Do you two wanna guess when that happens? … I'll give a dollar to the one who gets closest."

"Okay," said Thomas. "I'll say he flies in Alaska for the first time the next spring. I think he's probably too busy with school until then."

Kinley didn't hesitate. "I'll say he flies even before that," she said. "There's no way he makes it all the way until spring without flying."

"Who's right, Grandpa?" asked Thomas.

"I'm not telling you yet," Grandpa replied. "But let's talk more about what happens right after he gets to Fairbanks."

"What was the high school in Fairbanks like?" asked Kinley.

"It was pretty small," said Grandpa. "Picture a two-story wooden building with a pretty cool square belfry."

"What's a belfry?" asked Kinley.

"It's like a bell tower. I think I have a photo of a school with a bell tower to show you."

Grandpa showed them the photo.

Old school with belfry; *Author's Collection*

"Pretty neat," said Thomas.

"I think so too," said Grandpa, "There were 48 high school kids in the school, and *Mr. Eielson* was one of four teachers. There was another male teacher by the name of Mr. Keller—I couldn't find his first name. And there were two women teachers, Hannah Sponheim and Esther Smith. Carl Ben must have been pretty surprised when he saw Hannah there because she was from Hatton too."

"No way!" Thomas exclaimed.

"I thought the same thing," said Grandpa. "What were the chances of two teachers in Fairbanks being from the same little town of Hatton, North Dakota?"

"Less than one percent, for sure," said Kinley. "Is the high school still there?"

"No, it burned down in 1934," Grandpa answered. "It was fortunate Carl Ben had several days before school started because he definitely needed them. As a first-year teacher, he had a lot to learn about the subjects he was going to teach, the textbooks he would be using, preparing lessons, getting his room ready, and stuff like that. It was also lucky he had those three other teachers to help him out with any problems he had. But those days before school started were very exciting for Carl Ben. He had a great time exploring his new surroundings and meeting lots of people. With his great personality, he had an easy time making friends from the start."

Thomas chuckled. "And I'll bet all his new friends learned a lot about flying."

"Yes, they did," said Grandpa. "And Carl Ben learned a lot about dog sleds and many other things about Alaska."

"Was Carl Ben a good teacher?" asked Kinley.

"Without a doubt," replied Grandpa. "He must have been a busy teacher too, with all the challenges of being a first-year teacher plus his coaching responsibilities. But just imagine how much fun it must have been for his students to have a young, interesting guy like Mr. Eielson as their teacher."

"Did flying come up during their classroom discussions," asked Kinley.

"It sure did," said Grandpa, "and even the kids he coached in sports wanted to talk to him more about flying. There were discussions about the plusses and minuses of flying in Alaska, debates about using dog sleds versus planes, and stuff like that. Mr. Eielson even started teaching a new class on aviation at the high school later in the year. A group of kids also asked him to build a model airplane with them, and they did it."

"Like Carl Ben did after the Chautauqua," Kinley pointed out.

"That's right," said Grandpa.

"Was Carl Ben a good coach?" asked Thomas.

"Well," said Grandpa, "the high school basketball team he coached won a championship that year, and he helped develop a pretty good hockey team too."

"Did he meet any nice girls?" asked Kinley.

"He mentioned meeting a lot of girls at dances and stuff," Grandpa answered, "but most of them were married, and there were about three times as many men as women in Alaska at the time."

"When are you going to tell us about his flying?" asked Thomas. "I want to get that dollar you promised."

"All right," said Grandpa. "Let's just say it didn't take long for Carl Ben to get the Fairbanks people interested in flying. In fact, by the end of October, the Fairbanks City Council offered to chip in $1,000 for a plane, and a club in town called the Commercial Club would have probably paid the rest. By then, Carl Ben also had a good job offer to fly the next summer for a resort and mining company."

"But when does he actually fly in Alaska for the first time?" asked Kinley anxiously.

Grandpa said, "Kinley, you're probably going to like this more than Thomas does. Carl Ben flew for the first time during his first winter in Alaska, on February 21, 1923."

"I win!" Kinley exclaimed.

"I lose," Thomas said, smiling.

"Sorry, Thomas," said Grandpa, "Carl Ben was pretty anxious to prove that flying in cold winter conditions would work well in Alaska, especially for things like delivering mail and medical emergencies."

"How cold was it when he flew that first time?" asked Thomas.

"About five degrees," Grandpa replied. "He had a borrowed plane for this flight, and with the open cockpit on the plane, Carl Ben wore a warm Inuit parka and some boots called *mukluks* to keep his feet warm."

"Another great word, *mukluk*," said Kinley.

"A great name for a dog," Thomas added.

"I agree," said Grandpa, chuckling. "Anyway, this flight was historic. Carl Ben got permission to carry 500 pounds of mail for this 58-mile flight from Fairbanks to Nenana. It was the first unofficial air mail flight in Alaska, and it was under cold winter conditions. Many people doubted it was even possible. Before the flight, Carl Ben and his helpers did some special things to prepare the plane so the engine wouldn't freeze up, like warming up the oil before putting it in the engine and heating the engine itself."

"Did it go well?" asked Kinley.

"Yes, it did," answered Grandpa. "Carl Ben considered it an easy flight because he could just follow the railroad tracks the whole way. But lots of people were around to witness it in both towns, and they considered Carl Ben to be a real hero for what he did."

"When does Carl Ben fly his own plane in Alaska for the first time?" asked Thomas.

"I've got to tell you a little story about that," said

Grandpa. "Not long after he got to Fairbanks, Carl Ben met an old-timer named W. F. Thompson, the editor of the *News-Miner* newspaper. Carl Ben and W.F. Thompson had a lot of good discussions in the newspaper office about many things, especially flying in Alaska. Anyway, Carl Ben and Thompson became really good friends, and Thompson became a great supporter of Carl Ben's flying ambitions. In fact, it was because of the two men's discussions that Carl Ben came up with the idea of forming a company called the Farthest North Airplane Company, and W.F. Thompson became one of the investors."

"So, then the company bought a plane?" Thomas guessed.

"Yes, a war surplus Jenny," said Grandpa, "but it turned out buying a plane and then getting it to Alaska wasn't an easy thing to do. They knew it was critical to get it to Fairbanks by July 4 because they'd been offered $1,000 for stunt shows for that day—plus another huge event was taking place not long after that."

"What was that?" Kinley asked.

"The president of the United States was coming to Alaska," Grandpa replied, "and they thought that a Carl Ben flying exhibition could be part of that."

"Did they get the plane there on time?" asked Thomas.

"Barely," Grandpa answered. "The train carrying it pulled into Fairbanks on July 1, but they still had to assemble and test it before it would be ready for July 4."

"Was Carl Ben going to keep teaching?" asked Kinley.

"No," Grandpa answered. "This made him a little

sad, too, but he knew he had to pursue his dream of flying full-time in Alaska."

Aerial Photo of Fairbanks taken by Carl Ben; *State Historical Society of North Dakota*

CHAPTER 13

Flying His Own Plane

Grandpa said, "Carl Ben's plane arrived on July 1 in Fairbanks on a train in crates with lots of assembly required, so they didn't have much time to assemble it and get it ready for the big July 4, 1923, performances. Right away, Carl Ben got plenty of help getting the crates to the ballpark and assembling the plane. They worked all day, way out in the outfield, and Carl Ben got some special help from the best mechanic in town named Ira Farnsworth, who was especially skilled at putting the engine on the plane."

"It doesn't seem possible—assembling a plane and the flying it safely in just a few days," Thomas said.

"I thought the same thing," said Grandpa. "Let me tell you, there were lots of people watching that were pretty skeptical about whether the thing would fly or not after they finished assembling it. Some people were even heckling and making fun of Carl Ben and the others working on assembling the plane. There were even some placing bets on whether it would fly or not when they were done. It's pretty cool—Carl Ben's former students were probably the most positive supporters in the whole crowd."

"Hooray for his students!" Kinley exclaimed.

"That's what I say," said Grandpa. "So, they worked all that day, and then all day on July 2, and they got a lot done. Carl Ben was exhausted, and he slept under the plane on the second night."

"Just like he used to do," said Thomas.

"That's right," said Grandpa. "The goal for the next day, July 3, was to finish up by six that evening because there was a baseball game beginning at that time, and they needed to be out of the way. It's pretty funny, having enough sunlight to work wasn't really a problem up there in Alaska because there were 22 hours of daylight that time of the year."

"Pretty amazing," said Kinley.

"I can't imagine," said Grandpa. "Anyway, they didn't quite finish by six that evening, so the plane got towed way out in the outfield, out of the way of the baseball game. The game ended about eight-thirty, and the airplane assembly was still going on, so a lot of the baseball crowd gathered around to watch as the finishing touches were made in the assembly process. It wasn't long after that, Carl Ben announced that it was ready. Then a bunch of people helped push the plane out on the runway on the ballfield. Carl Ben got in the cockpit, and Farnsworth spun the propeller once to start the engine. ... Nothing happened. Farnsworth spun the propeller again. ... Oh no! Nothing happened!"

"I'll bet the third time was the charm," said Kinley.

"It was," said Grandpa. "Carl Ben took off and the

plane worked amazingly well. After that, he put on a flying show for the people watching from the ballfield and all the other people in Fairbanks that even impressed all those skeptics. He did some steep dives that *really* scared the crowd! It must have been one of the most memorable days *ever* in Fairbanks."

"I wish I could have been there," said Thomas.

"Me too," said Kinley.

"Me three," said Grandpa. "That night, two of Carl Ben's former students guarded the airplane so Carl Ben could get a good night's sleep at the hotel. The next day, Carl Ben couldn't believe it when he went back to the plane. Farnsworth had painted the word FAIRBANKS on the side of the plane in huge capital letters. I've got a good photo of the plane that was taken some time after that."

Grandpa showed them the photo.

"It looks like the landing didn't go too well there," Thomas said.

"As you'll see as we go along, landing planes in Alaska can be a real challenge," said Grandpa.

Carl Ben's plane; *State Historical Society of North Dakota*

"How did the Fourth of July go?" asked Kinley.

"It really couldn't have gone much better," replied Grandpa. "There were tons of people at the performance in Fairbanks, and a huge crowd in the town of Nenana too. Carl Ben put on stunt flying performances that were unforgettable, and I think he got many more people interested in flying. It didn't hurt that the newspapers in both towns printed very positive articles about Carl Ben's stunt flying that day. And W.F. Thompson printed some ads offering flying lessons and fun flights. ... Before I forget, I have to tell you about the flight that Carl Ben took to Nenana after the Fairbanks performance because it's pretty funny. Before he took off for Nenana that day, Carl Ben told his friend Mr. Wood that he needed him to fly along with him to Nenana to handle the financial stuff. Well, Mr. Wood was more than a little afraid at first, but he finally said he would go along. On the way to Fairbanks, Carl Ben gave Mr. Wood and a bunch of other people a pretty big thrill."

"What did Carl Ben do?" asked Thomas.

"Picture this. Remember, there were railroad tracks from Fairbanks to Nenana, and Carl Ben basically followed them on his flight. Well, there happened to be a train on the tracks that was also going to Nenana at this time, and Carl Ben decided to give the passengers and Mr. Wood a thrill. ... He decided to fly down to the level of the train and then fly past the windows and wave to the passengers."

"No way!" Thomas exclaimed.

"Too awesome!" said Kinley.

CHAPTER 14

President Harding Visits Alaska

Thomas said, "I'll bet business really took off after that for Carl Ben and the Farthest North Airplane Company."

"It did," said Grandpa, "but something happened about two weeks after July 4 that had a lot to do with it."

"The president's visit?" Kinley guessed.

"That's right," said Grandpa. "President Harding, our 29th president, came to Alaska with a bunch of other prominent people from the government, and Carl Ben was asked to perform flying stunts for them."

"Why was the president in Alaska?" asked Thomas.

Grandpa explained, "He was driving a golden spike to celebrate the completion of the Alaska Railway which ran about 480 miles from Seward to Fairbanks. It was part of a long trip that the president took beginning in June. When President Harding got to Seward on July 13, 1923, he boarded a special train that stopped at least nine times along the way. It was pretty cool, because First

PRESIDENT HARDING AND FIRST LADY FLORENCE HARDING IN CURRY, ALASKA; *AUTHOR'S COLLECTION*

PRESIDENT HARDING DRIVING THE GOLDEN SPIKE; *AUTHOR'S COLLECTION*

Lady Florence Harding was in the presidential party, and a future president was there too."

"Who?" asked Kinley.

"Let me give you a hint," said Grandpa. "Vacuum cleaner."

"Hoover!" Kinley and Thomas shouted at the same time.

"But President Herbert Hoover didn't really have anything to do with the vacuum cleaner," Grandpa added. "At this particular time, Hoover was serving in the president's cabinet as the secretary of commerce."

"Were the golden spikes actually made of gold?" asked Thomas.

"Yeah," added Kinley, "wouldn't someone steal them if they were made of gold?"

"That's a really good question that I don't know the answer to," said Grandpa. "I'm guessing they had a spike with some gold in it, and they pounded it in during a ceremony. Then they replaced it with an ordinary one later. The gold one probably went into a museum or something. Let's do some research on that later."

"Okay," said Thomas.

"So," Grandpa continued, "let me just say—Carl Ben put on an amazing performance for the president on July 15 in Fairbanks. He knew how important that performance was. Although the driving of the golden spike may have been a boost for railroad transportation in Alaska, Carl Ben was doing everything he could to show everyone that airplanes would be much more effective than trains covering the vast areas of Alaska for things like mail delivery, health emergencies, and other things. Carl Ben—*The Flying Professor*, they called him—

performed every stunt he knew, and he put on a great show. He was paid $1,000 in gold for his one-hour performance. ... It was particularly memorable for a lot of the people for another reason besides the stunts that Carl Ben performed. It was 94 degrees that day, and three people collapsed from the heat. I guess some of the people in the presidential party were a little overdressed. They thought it never got that hot in Alaska, and they'd been told to prepare for colder weather."

"Ninety-four degrees is pretty rare in North Dakota, too," said Thomas.

"That's for sure," said Grandpa. "When Carl Ben was done flying, the president and several other officials in his party shook hands with Carl Ben. They were definitely impressed with Carl Ben and what he'd shown them."

Kinley said, "Grandpa, I think I remember our teacher telling us something weird that happened to President Harding."

"That's right," said Grandpa. "Harding died in San Francisco shortly after he left Alaska when he was returning to Washington. He was only president for about two and a half years. He was a heavy smoker, and he was also overweight, and I think he died of a heart attack."

"Wow!" Thomas exclaimed. "Did President Harding serve the least time of any president?"

"No," Grandpa answered, "that would be Zachary Taylor, the twelfth president. He only served as president for about 16 months."

"What happened to him?" asked Kinley.

"He died of a stomach virus or something," Grandpa

answered. "That's something else we can research later if you'd like."

Kinley chuckled. "We're developing quite a list of things to research later," she said.

President Zachary Taylor; *Author's Collection*

CHAPTER 15

First Summer of Business in Alaska

Thomas said, "Carl Ben couldn't have gotten better publicity for his business than the president's visit."

"It was huge!" said Grandpa. "Right away, a lawyer working for a mining company hired Carl Ben to fly him to a mine on Stewart Creek, about an hour flying time away from Fairbanks. There was some mail and some machine parts that were needed at the mine onboard the plane too. This was the first commercial flight *ever* in the interior of Alaska—a really big deal."

"It must be beautiful flying over Alaska," said Kinley.

"I've flown over the state a few times," said Grandpa. "With all that breathtaking landscape below him, I'll bet it was hard for Carl Ben to pay close attention and not get lost. Remember, he didn't have all those fancy navigational instruments on his plane like they have now. The lawyer and Carl Ben had to fly by the seat of their pants, trying to recognize key landmarks down below as they were flying along. But they got there with no problems. And after that, word spread quickly about Carl Ben's flight—with F.W. Thompson's help, of course. After that, business was so great, Carl Ben paid for the plane in just ten days."

"And business got even better?" Kinley guessed.

"That's right," said Grandpa. "Carl Ben's great personality sure didn't hurt. People started hiring Carl Ben to fly for a bunch of different reasons that summer. Carl Ben called himself an *errand boy with wings*. He delivered groceries, mail, machine parts, and supplies. He was also *sort of* a flying newsboy because he could share the latest news with the people wherever he flew. And Carl Ben got special satisfaction when he flew for one particular purpose."

"What was that?" asked Thomas.

"To help sick people?" Kinley guessed.

"You're right," said Grandpa, smiling. "With the huge distances involved and the rough terrain, Carl Ben could make a big difference helping sick people who lived a long way from a doctor or hospital. Sometimes he flew the doctor to the patients, and sometimes he flew the patients to the hospital in Fairbanks. Either way, he saved lives. He called these flights *mercy flights*, and Carl Ben loved them."

"His dad must have been proud when he heard about that," said Thomas.

"He sure was," said Grandpa.

"Did Carl Ben have any major problems that summer?" Kinley asked.

Grandpa said, "Amazingly, there was only one major problem worth mentioning that could have ended up bad for Carl Ben, but it didn't. That whole summer, he and his mechanics did a great job of keeping the plane in excellent flying condition, but the plane got a real workout. It flew about 145 hours that summer—12,000 miles or so—and there were quite a few rough landings, so the landing gear had to be replaced several times. With all that, there was only one time the plane got in real trouble that summer. It happened on a flight to Circle City, a town just 50 miles from the Arctic Circle, about 160 miles from Fairbanks. Circle City was so far away, they had to install an auxiliary fuel tank on the plane before the trip so Carl Ben could fly that far."

"Why was Carl Ben flying to Circle City?" asked Thomas.

"A mine there had a real problem with water flooding it," Grandpa explained. "Carl Ben was taking them a heavy pump so they could pump the water out. He had some other supplies with him too. Anyway, Carl Ben was flying there, and as usual, he always looked down as he flew and tried to spot places he could land if he needed to. Well, just 20 miles from the mine in Circle City, he needed to land."

"What happened?" Kinley asked.

"The engine began sputtering, and the plane began losing altitude. Carl Ben immediately landed safely on a beach-like area next to a creek that he had spotted earlier, but now he had *another* problem. He wasn't the best mechanic, but he immediately did what he knew to get the engine running again. Now there was just one big problem left."

"The planes' wheels were broken?" Thomas guessed.

"No," said Grandpa, "but that's a great guess. Big

swarms of hungry mosquitos were attacking him. He swatted them as he worked as fast as he could, and then he ran to the area he would need to use to take off. Then he cleared brush and stuff that would be in the way. After that, he got in the cockpit. Thank goodness the engine started—and he took off, brushing the trees as he ascended into the sky. He arrived in Circle City only about 45 minutes behind schedule."

"Did Carl Ben ever get a new plane?" asked Kinley.

"That's a great question," said Grandpa. "By this time, winter was approaching, and Carl Ben was getting a little frustrated that he couldn't fly even farther around Alaska with his plane—plus it needed to be replaced. He obviously needed a bigger, better plane. He tried writing letters to his friend Dan Sutherland in Washington, D.C. He also contacted some people in the United States Postal Department, trying to get a mail contract from them that would help pay for a bigger, better De Havilland plane, but he didn't get a positive response from them. So, after the first snowfall in Fairbanks, Carl Ben decided he needed to go to Washington, D.C., in person and see what he could do."

"And he talks them into a bigger plane, doesn't he?" said Thomas.

CHAPTER 16

Alaskan Airmail History

"Yes, he got a new plane," said Grandpa. "On the way to Washington, D.C., he even got a chance to stop in Hatton to see his family and friends."

"Did Carl Ben have a good time in Hatton?" asked Kinley.

"He sure did," Grandpa replied. "As you can expect, Carl Ben's dad brought up the subject of going back to school, but Carl Ben reiterated his plans to keep on flying in Alaska."

"What's *reiterated* mean?" asked Thomas.

"It means to say something over again with special emphasis," said Grandpa.

"I like the sound when I say *reiterate*," said Thomas. "*I like the sound when I say reiterate,*" Thomas repeated in a louder voice.

"Me too ... *Me too,*" said Kinley, giggling.

"You two are way too *precocious*," said Grandpa.

"Anyway, when Carl Ben finally got to Washington, D.C., his friend Dan Sutherland helped convince the Post Office Department to give Carl Ben the mail contract plus a new plane. It sure didn't hurt that President Harding had recently visited Alaska, plus many of Harding's cabinet members and others in government knew who Carl Ben was, and they supported his efforts. It also didn't hurt that Carl Ben was a hard man to say *no* to. He had that great personality, and his debating ability came in pretty handy too. Carl Ben got a new De Havilland plane plus a contract for 10 round trips between the Alaskan towns of Fairbanks and McGrath, a distance of about 300 miles. I guess those 10 trips would be a good test of the feasibility of air mail service in Alaska. McGrath didn't even have a landing area, but Carl Ben knew he could easily land on the frozen river nearby. … Well, they got everything ready for the first official airmail flight on February 21, 1924, exactly one year after that first flight Carl Ben made from Fairbanks to Nenana."

"Grandpa? Why am I getting a feeling the first flight didn't go so well?" said Thomas.

"Because you can read my mind," said Grandpa, chuckling. "It mostly went well, but there definitely was a problem that could have led to real tragedy. Here's what happened from the beginning. Before the plane took off, a dog sled pulled up beside Carl Ben in the plane, and there were lots of photos taken. It was a neat photo that captured the historic moment and contrasted the two methods of mail delivery in Alaska. I can show you a photo of that event."

Grandpa showed them the photo.

First official airmail flight in Alaska; *State Historical Society of North Dakota*

"How much mail was Carl Ben carrying on the plane?" asked Kinley.

"One hundred sixty-four pounds of it," Grandpa answered, "and he had lots of other stuff on board, too—a bunch of tools, enough food and supplies for about 10 days in case something happened, some extra gas and oil, some spare parts, a gun, an axe, and some snowshoes."

"What was he wearing to keep warm?" Thomas asked.

"Well, it was five below zero, so he definitely needed to keep warm in the plane with that open cockpit. He had lots of layers, just like we wear when it's below zero, topped off with a reindeer skin parka with wolverine fur. He was wearing his mukluk boots that went over his knees, a cap, and some goggles. The plane took off at

8:45 in the morning on that first *official* airmail flight in Alaska *ever*."

"How exciting!" Kinley exclaimed.

"It definitely was, and the flight to McGrath went really well. The compass on the plane wasn't working correctly because of the magnetism of the plane's engine, but Carl Ben could see the landmarks like rivers and lakes and Mt. McKinley clearly, so he could stay on the correct flight pattern. On the way to McGrath, something really awesome happened. Carl Ben flew over Fred Milligan on his dog sled with Milligan's team of dogs pulling the sled through the snow. Fred Milligan was delivering mail the old-fashioned way. Believe it or not, the same mail route Carl Ben could do in about seven hours of flight time took Fred Milligan about 20 days or more. Carl Ben waved as he flew over Fred. Just imagine what the two men must have been thinking."

Thomas said, "Fred probably wondered if his work delivering mail with a dog sled was almost over."

Kinley chuckled and said, "His dogs must have wondered what kind of noisy bird that was."

Grandpa laughed. "Well," he said, "Carl Ben got to McGrath in great time—two hours and 50 minutes, and he was anxious to return to Fairbanks right away, but here's where the problem started. The people of McGrath wanted to celebrate, and Carl Ben decided not to disappoint them. That meant he would probably be making his return trip while it was getting dark."

"Why didn't he just stay overnight?" asked Thomas.

"The people actually asked him to do just that," said Grandpa, "but Carl Ben was worried about his plane sitting out all night in that cold weather and the engine not starting the next morning."

"And then he gets lost in the dark on the way back, doesn't he?" said Kinley, looking worried.

"Yes, he does," Grandpa answered. "He didn't get out of McGrath until after 2:00 p.m., and that meant he would have to fly part of the time on the way back in the dark if he was delayed at all."

"When does the sun set that time of the year?" Thomas asked.

"At 5:42 p.m.," said Grandpa. "Carl Ben got to the halfway point just fine, which was Lake Minchumina, but it was getting dark already by then. Not long after that, Fred Milligan heard the plane in the distance, and he sensed Carl Ben was not on course—and he wasn't. He was about 50 miles *off* course. Carl Ben realized he was in trouble when he flew over a river that wasn't on the map he was using. After a while, he was flying in complete darkness. It was cloudy, too, so there was no help from the moon and stars."

"And he must have been running out of gas," said Thomas.

"Now what?" asked Kinley.

"Well, it wasn't good," said Grandpa, "but Carl Ben knew trying to land in the dark wouldn't be smart at all, so he kept in the air, hoping. … Then he spotted a light! He thought it might be a trapper's cabin on the Chatanika River, so he instinctively turned left, and it turned out to be the right move."

"I'm so glad," said Kinley, relieved.

Grandpa continued, "And not long after, he spotted the home field in Fairbanks. It was well lit with flares in empty barrels, something Carl Ben had recommended be done just in case something like this happened."

"I'll bet there were a lot of happy people," said Thomas.

"Yes, there were," said Grandpa. "It was about 6:30 by then, so people were really worried. Some were even crying. When that first person heard the plane approaching, you can imagine how excited he was. But there was a problem when Carl Ben landed. The flares were not quite in the right places so he couldn't clearly see the safest area to land. He ended up hitting a tree, breaking the landing gear, breaking one of the skis, and smashing the propeller. Carl Ben had landed with one gallon of gas left. He had been in the air four hours and 10 minutes, way too much of that time in the dark."

"Carl Ben sure keeps us in suspense," said Thomas.

"He sure does," said Grandpa. "And Carl Ben's account of that first official airmail flight in Alaska was read at the president's cabinet meeting in Washington, D.C."

"Who was president then?" asked Kinley.

"Coolidge," said Grandpa. "Herbert Hoover was still the Secretary of Commerce, and he would become the next president in 1928. Hoover even sent a letter of congratulations to Carl Ben after that flight."

CHAPTER 17

Carl Ben's Airmail Flights

CARL BEN AND HIS PLANE; *STATE HISTORICAL SOCIETY OF NORTH DAKOTA*

"I hope the rest of the flights went better than the first one," said Thomas.

"Well," said Grandpa, "there's some good news about that and some bad news. Which do you want to hear first?"

"Good news!" Kinley exclaimed.

"Me too," said Thomas. "I just hope the bad news isn't too bad."

"It isn't," said Grandpa. "But I'll have to jump ahead to the fifth trip on April 19 for the good news. Something pretty awesome happened on that one. When Carl Ben landed in McGrath, there were several Inuit waiting for him, and they wanted to do a *potlatch* ceremony to honor him."

"What's that?" asked Kinley.

"It's a gift-giving ceremony that is used to celebrate special occasions. The first thing the Inuit did during the ceremony was to have a big feast with foods like caribou and fish. After that, they presented Carl Ben with a new parka. Then they did something that left him speechless. They adopted him and gave him the name *Moose Ptarmigan Ben.*"

"What's a ptarmigan?" asked Thomas.

"It's a bird," Grandpa answered. "I think I have a photo of one here someplace."

Grandpa showed them the photo on his computer.

PTARMIGAN; *AUTHOR'S COLLECTION*

Grandpa explained, "The ptarmigan was the swiftest bird known by the Inuit people, and the moose was one of the biggest animals they knew about."

Kinley said, "And they probably thought of Carl Ben as a very big person—not in his size, but in his achievements?"

"That's right," said Grandpa.

Thomas said, "That must have been a great day for Carl Ben. Now, what about the bad news?"

"Okay," said Grandpa. "Unfortunately, Carl Ben never made it to the tenth flight. He didn't get hurt or anything, but it wasn't good."

"What happened?" asked Thomas.

"On Carl Ben's sixth trip, he did something he wasn't supposed to do, and it led to a real problem. When Carl Ben flew to McGrath, a group of miners were waiting there with a very sick man that needed to be flown to the Fairbanks Hospital. Carl Ben wasn't supposed to fly passengers with the mail. It wasn't part of his contract—but he couldn't turn the men down. However, that meant flying with quite a bit of extra weight, and when he landed in Fairbanks on a soggy field, the plane was damaged."

"How bad?" asked Kinley.

"A ski broke, then the plane skidded along a big ditch," said Grandpa. "The nose of the plane went down, and the propeller snapped. The sick passenger ended up hanging upside down for a while, but he was okay."

"Did the man live after they took him to the hospital?" asked Thomas.

"I think so," replied Grandpa, "but Carl Ben had to report to Washington, D.C., after each trip he made, so they eventually found out about what happened. Carl

Ben informed them why he had made the life-and-death decision and everything, but that led to something pretty bad that happened in May on the eighth trip."

"Oh no!" said Kinley.

"It wasn't good," said Grandpa. "This time Carl Ben carried another passenger who was very ill by the name of Charlie Nystrom from the town of Iditarod."

"Isn't the Iditarod a race with dog sleds?" asked Thomas.

"Yes, it is," said Grandpa. "The race was actually named after the Iditarod Trail. The Iditarod Trail was named after the town of Iditarod, which was named after the Iditarod River that runs through it."

Thomas giggled, "I think I get all that."

"Anyway," said Grandpa, "on this eighth trip, Carl Ben flew Charlie from Iditarod, and when they landed in Fairbanks, they hit a soggy spot again. After that, the plane sank way down in the mud and crashed on its side. And this time, Carl Ben lost his airmail contract after the people in Washington, D.C., got his report."

"Now what?" asked Kinley.

"Carl Ben didn't let it get him down too much," Grandpa replied. "After that, he flew for a guy named Jimmy Rodebaugh who had purchased two planes, and Jimmy also had two other pilots working for him. Carl Ben did that for the whole next summer, and it went well. But he still wanted to get some permanent airmail contracts for Alaska. He wrote letters to all the people he could. He even went to New York City to try to get some private funding for planes he could use to try to get those airmail contracts. After that, he went on to Washington, D.C., but the people in charge of making those decisions weren't in favor of flying at that time."

"Because of what Carl Ben did?" asked Kinley.

"Maybe that was part of it," said Grandpa," but a lot of them still considered flying to be a fad, plus there was the problem of Billy Mitchell who tried to fly around the world about this time, and one of his planes crashed in Alaska."

"The Black Squadron guy?" asked Thomas.

"That's right," said Grandpa. "The plane crash was fresh in people's minds. So, after that, Carl Ben decided to go back to North Dakota for a while. Then Ole tried to talk Carl Ben into going back to Georgetown to finish his law degree, and Carl Ben actually went back."

"I'm guessing that didn't last long," said Kinley.

"Three weeks," Grandpa answered. "After that, Carl Ben joined the Army Air Service testing the skis on planes. ... But then something happened in Alaska in January of 1925 that changed a lot of people's attitudes about flying there."

"What?" asked Thomas.

"Diphtheria happened in Nome," said Grandpa. "And lots of children were dying."

"What's diphtheria?" asked Kinley.

"It's an awful respiratory disease, so it affects the lungs," said Grandpa, "and the Inuit didn't have a lot of resistance to it. There was a serum that could fight the disease, but it needed to get from Nenana to Nome as fast as possible. The people in charge didn't trust flying because they were worried about the plane going down and the serum being lost. So, an incredible thing happened back then. Sled dog teams performed an amazing relay race called The Great Race of Mercy to get a 20-pound package of serum 674 miles from Nenana to Nome. It's hard to even imagine how amazing that sled dog relay must have been! It involved 19 dog teams, 150 dogs, 127-and-a-half hours, which is about five-and-a-half days. The relay was run through the freezing cold, treacherous conditions of winter in Alaska. That Iditarod Race we talked about is run every year to honor their awesome achievement. ... A dog named Balto led the dog sled team on the final leg of the relay into Nome, and he became a national hero. He has a statue in New York City's Central Park, and they even made a movie about the great sled dog relay with Balto as the star."

"Please show us a photo of Balto," said Kinley.

Grandpa showed them a few photos.

BALTO STATUE IN CENTRAL PARK; *AUTHOR'S COLLECTION*

Balto and his musher, Gunnar Kaasen;
Author's Collection

"And after that relay," said Grandpa, "people also realized flying would have been a lot faster and would have saved many more lives—so flying in Alaska became more of an accepted thing. And that helped Carl Ben's efforts."

CHAPTER 18

The Detroit Expedition

"Did Carl Ben get those mail contracts he wanted?" asked Thomas.

"Well," said Grandpa, "at least the Post Office Department started moving toward airmail service for Alaska. By the end of the year 1925, Carl Ben submitted some bids for providing that service. But then he had to wait to see if his bids would be accepted. He decided to go home to Hatton while the government was making its decision."

"What are bids again?" asked Kinley.

"Think of it as Carl Ben making his best offer for providing airmail service on different routes in Alaska—how much he would charge the government for that service. To make enough to pay for everything and make a profit, he'd have to figure in things like the cost of the airplanes, the fuel, the upkeep, the pilots' salaries, and his own living expenses. Remember, other people could make bids too, and the government would then choose which bid they liked the best."

"Do they always pick the lowest bid?" asked Kinley.

"No," said Grandpa. "Sometimes the people submitting the lowest bid are found not to be the best to do the job."

Thomas asked, "When Carl Ben went home, did Ole try to talk him into going back to school again?"

"No," Grandpa replied, "but Carl Ben's brother Oliver talked him into traveling around North Dakota selling bonds."

"What are bonds?" asked Kinley.

"They're a little like fancy IOUs," said Grandpa. "Someone sells you a bond for an amount of money, let's say $100. You pay him $100 and get a fancy piece of paper that says he will pay you all your money back with some extra money for you called *interest* after a certain amount of time."

"Sounds pretty boring," said Kinley. "I'm guessing Carl Ben didn't sell bonds very long."

Grandpa chuckled. "You're right again, Kinley," he said. "Carl Ben sold bonds for about two months. Then one day he was getting a haircut in Langdon, North Dakota, when he got a message from his dad. A man named Captain George Hubert Wilkins had sent a telegram to Hatton. Captain Wilkins wanted Carl Ben to be a pilot on an exciting Arctic expedition that he was leading."

"Who was Captain Wilkins?" asked Thomas.

"He was a pretty amazing young man," replied Grandpa. "He was only 37 at the time, and like Carl Ben, he had done a lot during his life already. He was a hero during World War I, fighting for his country, Australia. He had flown airplanes, and he was an excellent navigator too. He had also explored large areas of the Arctic and Antarctica, mostly on the ground. Besides all of that, he was a pioneer in aerial photography. Here's a good photo of him."

Captain Wilkins, *Author's Collection*

"What did Captain Wilkins want to accomplish on the Arctic expedition?" asked Kinley.

"Carl Ben traveled to New York City to meet with Wilkins and find that out," Grandpa explained. "When he got there, Wilkins told Carl Ben all about his big plans for what he called the Detroit Arctic Expedition."

"What did Detroit have to do with it?" asked Thomas.

Grandpa explained, "It was named that because Wilkins had received financial backing from a bunch of people from Detroit, including the school children who had collected pennies for the expedition. I guess Detroit was already the automobile capital of the world, and they wanted to become the aeronautical capital of the world too, designing and building the best airplanes anywhere."

"Do you know how many pennies the Detroit children collected?" asked Kinley.

"No," answered Grandpa, "but I'll bet it was a lot. I think I read that almost 200,000 Detroit children were involved. … Anyway, Wilkins told Carl Ben that a huge part of his plan involved exploring the area north of Point Barrow, Alaska, all the way up to the North Pole. Most of that huge area had never been explored before by air. They would have two monoplanes built by a Dutch company with *closed* cabins this time, thank goodness. They would fly from Fairbanks to Barrow with 40,000 pounds of supplies and then set up a supply depot in Barrow for their Arctic flights. After that, they would fly from there, over the Arctic Ocean, exploring that huge region of the Arctic that was unexplored. They would take another trip and plant the American flag after they landed on the ice. From there, they would fly over the North Pole to a place called Spitsbergen."

"Grandpa," said Thomas, "I don't mind cold weather when I dress warm and everything, but I can't imagine flying over a region that's unexplored in freezing cold weather when lots of bad things can happen, especially if the plane goes down for some reason."

"Yeah," said Kinley. "I sure hope nothing bad happens to Carl Ben and Captain Wilkins and everyone else involved in the Detroit Expedition."

Grandpa grimaced. "Let me promise you this—Carl Ben and Captain Wilkins survive the Arctic Expedition, but they go through some things you will never forget!"

CHAPTER 19

What Else Can Possibly Go Wrong?

Grandpa said, "The Detroit Arctic Expedition definitely had more than its share of mishaps and unbelievable challenges. Let's start with that first year, 1926, and you'll get a really good taste of all the things Carl Ben and the other men on the expedition went through. Many of Carl Ben's friends didn't even want him to fly in this expedition. They knew how risky it was going to be flying over unknown regions where you could have engine problems anytime. Then, even if you landed safely, you might never be found. There were no maps available for much of the area and no weather reports, and that made things even riskier. Heck, much of the land they hoped to explore was called The Blind Spot of the Arctic, which gives you an idea just how mysterious and unknown it was."

"But Carl Ben loved stuff like this," said Thomas.

"And so did Wilkins," said Grandpa. "Carl Ben told his worried friends he knew he could land somewhere if he needed to, and then Wilkins and he could live off the land for a long time after the plane went down. They would make sure to have adequate supplies onboard the plane, including a gun so they could hunt for fresh meat. And they could always build a snow house for shelter."

Kinley cringed. "So how long did it take before bad stuff started to happen?"

"Not long," said Grandpa. "By March 11, 1926, the two planes were put together in Fairbanks and ready to test. Carl Ben was a little down because another pilot named Major Lamphier was chosen to make the test run with the larger of the two planes, the *Detroiter*. Well, before the plane even got off the ground, the wheels *kinda* got stuck on a snowdrift, so some men ran over and packed down the snow, then pushed the plane to get it moving so it could take off. That's when something *awful* happened. A newspaperman named Palmer Hutchinson from Detroit was anxious to help out, but when he was pushing, he somehow got in the way of the moving propeller."

"Oh no!" Kinley exclaimed.

"Yes, it was really sad and tragic," said Grandpa. "The man died, and that also shut the expedition down for about a week. After that, Captain Wilkins chose Carl Ben to be the pilot this time for a test run involving the smaller plane, the *Alaskan*. Captain Wilkins went along, and Carl Ben was determined to have a good flight."

"But it crashed?" Kinley guessed.

"Well," Grandpa said, "the short flight went well, but the landing—not so much. The engine stalled at around 200 feet as they were coming in for a landing, then Carl Ben tried to increase power and climb out of it, but it was too late."

The Detroiter; *State Historical Society of North Dakota*

"He crashed!?" Thomas exclaimed.

"Yes, he did," said Grandpa. "Both men were okay, but the plane hit a fence and there was quite a bit of damage to the propeller and landing gear. It would take at least two or three weeks to fix, and they were rapidly running out of the best flying time to accomplish some of the goals of the Detroit Arctic Expedition. Carl Ben thought he was going to be fired after that, but Wilkins didn't say anything bad about the crash to him. However, when the *Detroiter* was going for a test flight soon after that, Wilkins chose Major Lamphier to do the flying. Then another unbelievable thing happened."

"Crash!?" Thomas and Kinley both yelled at the same time.

"Yup," said Grandpa. "Almost the exact thing happened to Major Lamphier as happened to Carl Ben—a stall at about 200 feet and a crash."

"Anyone fired this time?" asked Thomas.

"Nope," Grandpa replied. "Now, turn the clock

ahead to March 30, just 12 days after Carl Ben's accident. The *Alaskan* was fixed, and Captain Wilkins told Carl Ben they were going for a short flight to test her out. Well, that short flight went well, and Wilkins surprised Carl Ben. He told him they were going to fly to Barrow the next day. Finally, they would have a chance to accomplish something *really* big. Imagine—over six hours flight time—a 500-mile flight—the first *ever* flight from Fairbanks to Barrow—over land that had never ever been flown over. But it would be *extremely* dangerous. Again, remember, the weather would be a huge factor, and there were really no maps to fly by. Thank goodness Carl Ben would have Captain Wilkins along because he was a really good navigator."

"Did it go well?" asked Kinley.

"It was phenomenal!" said Grandpa. "The men shared a six-hour adventure flying over unbelievable scenery. All of Carl Ben's flying skills and Captain Wilkins' navigation skills were needed to fly over mountains, through narrow mountain passes, past rock walls, through the heavy fog, and over the tundra, with blizzard conditions on the ground below. The only signs of human life were a few little Inuit settlements along the way. When they got to Barrow, Wilkins had Carl Ben keep flying, and they flew over the Arctic Ocean for about an hour. This was an area that no one had ever flown over. Eventually, they flew back to Barrow and landed near a trading post in a blizzard. … I've got some photos from the Detroit Arctic Expedition that you're going to like."

Grandpa showed them the photos.

The Alaskan; *State Historical Society of North Dakota*

Carl Ben and the Alaskan; *State Historical Society of North Dakota*

Carl Ben and Wilkins with an unidentified cameraman; *State Historical Society of North Dakota*

Carl Ben leaning up against the Alaskan; *State Historical Society of North Dakota*

The *Alaskan* taking off; *State Historical Society of North Dakota*

Carl Ben and a woman near the plane; *State Historical Society of North Dakota*

PULLING THE PLANE THROUGH THE MUD; *STATE HISTORICAL SOCIETY OF NORTH DAKOTA*

Kinley pointed at the photo with Carl Ben and the woman. "Who is that lady?" she asked.

"I'm not sure," said Grandpa, "but she sure is pretty."

"Yes, she is," said Kinley.

"And nothing went wrong on that flight?" asked Thomas.

"Not on that flight," said Grandpa. "I must tell you, though, they made another flight from Fairbanks to Barrow in late April, and things didn't go quite as well."

"What do you mean?" asked Kinley.

"Well," said Grandpa, "in late April, they made a second flight with freight to Barrow. The flight there was okay, but on the way back to Fairbanks, a fire destroyed the canvas covering the motor, and Wilkins broke his arm spinning the propeller. But, otherwise, they made it back to Fairbanks okay. The important thing was, they got a bunch of supplies up to Barrow so they could use it as a base for future exploration of the Arctic. Also, Carl

Ben and Wilkins really developed a good relationship on those flights—something that would prove valuable later. Unfortunately, that was the end of their flying for that year. The good flying time in the Arctic was over. Also, it was a little sad for Carl Ben and Wilkins. Other explorers had accomplished what the Detroit Expedition had wanted to—they had flown over the North Pole."

"Who did that?" asked Thomas.

Grandpa said, "A guy named Admiral Byrd did it with a plane, and Roald Amundsen did it with a dirigible. I have a photo of Amundsen's dirigible."

Amundsen's Dirigible Norge; *Author's Collection*

"What does Carl Ben do after that?" asked Thomas.

Grandpa looked at Kinley with a big smile. "Kinley, you will like this. I found out he spent some of his time after that dating a nice teacher from Fairbanks named Marie Banks."

"Then that might have been her in that photo," said Kinley, excitedly.

"That's right," said Grandpa. "And you're not going to believe what Carl Ben did next. He got word that there was a job waiting for him in Florida, so he went there and spent the summer of 1926 flying airmail flights. He even flew the first airmail plane between Jacksonville and Atlanta, and he flew mail between several other cities in Florida too."

"Talk about a huge change in climate," said Thomas.

"That's for sure," said Grandpa. "Carl Ben thought the same thing many times as he flew over the Everglades, watching a bunch of alligators down below, while he was wearing just shorts and a T-shirt. He really enjoyed the experience down South, but it didn't take long before he missed Alaska. He was glad when Captain Wilkins contacted him and said he'd raised enough money to continue the Arctic Expedition for a second year."

CHAPTER 20

I Can't Believe They Survived That

"This next part of Carl Ben's story is amazing!" said Grandpa. "I've gotta tell you, though, it makes me shiver just thinking about it. I've also gotta tell you before I start—Carl Ben and Captain Wilkins go through an ordeal that's hard to believe, but they somehow get through it all."

Kinley looked at Grandpa and smiled. "Do we need some homemade hot chocolate to help us get through it?"

Grandpa chuckled. "That's a great idea, Kinley. Let's make some right now, using our old family recipe, before I start getting into the story. Kinley, you get the cocoa out. Thomas, you get that saucepan we use for making cocoa. I'll get the sugar."

Kinley said, "I know the directions by heart. We need two heaping tablespoons of pure cocoa and four heaping tablespoons of sugar. Then we dissolve the cocoa and sugar in just enough water to fully dissolve it. We bring it to a rolling boil for one minute, then reduce the heat to medium. We add eight cups of milk and heat it up to the desired temperature."

"Perfect," said Grandpa. "And we should have plenty of hot chocolate to have seconds if we want."

After they were done making the hot chocolate, Grandpa used a ladle to fill three large mugs, and they settled down at the table again.

Grandpa took a sip and began. "Wow, that's good! ... So, by late February of 1927, Carl Ben was back in Fairbanks."

"And back with his girlfriend, Marie Banks?" asked Kinley.

"Yes," answered Grandpa, "and there were now some new people and planes involved with the expedition. They had two new Stinson biplanes with skis on them called *Detroit News Number 1* and *Detroit News Number 2*. There was also a new pilot working with Carl Ben named Alger Graham. Fortunately, they had transported enough gasoline and supplies to Barrow the year before, so now they could fly out of Barrow to explore the Arctic. The immediate plan was to fly north and west to a specific spot, 78 degrees north latitude and 180 degrees longitude. Then they would land the plane on the sea ice in the Arctic, something that no pilot had never been done before, and they would take what are called *soundings*."

"What are *soundings*?" asked Thomas.

Grandpa explained, "It's a way to figure out how deep the water is when you can't just use a weighted rope and drop it into the water because it could be *really* deep—maybe as deep as several miles. In this case they had some equipment including some small explosives so they could bounce sound off the bottom of the ocean and back to the plane, then they would figure out how long it took the echo to get back up to the surface. Then I guess they did some fancy mathematics, and they were able to determine both how far the sound traveled and the depth of the ocean. It's a lot like sonar works, I think. … Anyway, the plan was to take some soundings after they landed on the ice, then if they found the ocean to be shallow, they would hopefully continue toward any land area that might be nearby. If the water turned out to be *really* deep, they would fly farther south about 200 miles and take another sounding. Hopefully, they would find evidence of there being land not too far under the ice somewhere.

"So, it took a while before they had all they needed for that first flight, but on March 29, they were ready. The plane named *Detroit News Number 1* was ready to go. Once Captain Wilkins and Carl Ben got up into the air at about 6:00 a.m., they noticed it was 32 below zero outside and 18 degrees in the cabin. Several Inuit watched the plane take off, and they were amazed that the plane was heading north. To them, the plane was headed to *the land of never come back.*"

"That doesn't sound good," said Thomas. "But you assured us Carl Ben and Captain Wilkins come back."

"Yes, they do," said Grandpa. "As the plane flew north, Carl Ben had some thoughts about the huge difference between this and his recent flying in Florida."

"Yeah," said Kinley. "More than 100 degrees difference outside."

"That's right," said Grandpa, "So, anyway, they flew north out of Barrow, over the Arctic Ocean ice. One hour out they noticed large pans of ice, some even large enough to land on. As they flew farther, though, they noticed the ice had more cracks and edges. If there was an emergency, that would make it much more dangerous to land and then take off again. For about six hours and 450 miles, everything was going well on their flight, but then they noticed the engine started missing and sputtering."

"Oh no!" Thomas exclaimed.

"Did they have to land?" asked Kinley.

"Yup," said Grandpa, "they knew they had to land and fix the engine."

"I don't like this," said Kinley.

"It wasn't good," said Grandpa. "But, somehow, Carl Ben was able to use his great skill and glide the plane in and land on a large patch of rough ice—something that many people thought couldn't be done. Right away, Carl Ben got out and worked on the engine while Captain Wilkins made a sounding, and he determined the depth of the ocean there was three miles, the deepest ever recorded in the Arctic."

"Were they able to take off right after that?" asked Kinley.

"Well," said Grandpa, "Carl Ben worked on the engine for two hours, and both Wilkins and Carl Ben wondered if they'd ever be able to get off the ice. When Carl Ben was finished, they got on board and the engine started."

"Thank goodness," said Kinley.

"Yes," said Grandpa, "and fortunately, they were able to lift off the rough ice successfully in a storm, even though it didn't happen until the fifth attempt."

"Great job, Carl Ben!" Thomas exclaimed.

"It definitely was," said Grandpa. "Then Carl Ben and Captain Wilkins decided they needed to head back to Barrow because it was already getting dark and difficult to navigate because a big storm was covering the sun, and a strong wind was blowing the plane around. They weren't in the air very long, and both men could tell the engine wasn't working the way it should be."

"Don't tell me they had to land *again*," said Thomas.

"They knew they had to," said Grandpa. "The engine made some sputtering noises and almost stalled. Fortunately, Carl Ben was able to make an incredible landing on a large pan of ice under awful conditions. He worked on the engine as quickly as possible, taking off his gloves and exposing his fingers to 40 below zero temperatures way too long."

"Grandpa, he could get frostbite that way!" Kinley said, looking worried.

"That's right," said Grandpa. "We all know how hard that must have been for Carl Ben to expose his skin like that, but he had a choice between frozen fingers and possibly never getting off the ice again. On the positive side, he was able to get the plane's engine working again, then he flew it off the ice on the second try—with almost no room to spare."

"Grandpa," said Kinley, grimacing, "I want to find out what happens next, but I know it's not good."

"Well," said Grandpa, "it was now 2:00 p.m., and they figured with some luck, they could get back to Barrow before dark. They still had enough gasoline for eight hours of flight, and Carl Ben got the plane up to an altitude above the blizzard, about 4,000 feet or so. But there was virtually no visibility, with a blizzard going on down below them. They were eating pemmican and biscuits with coffee along the way."

"What's *pemmican*?" asked Thomas.

"It's an Inuit food," said Grandpa. "I have no idea what it tastes like, but it's supposedly a paste-like food that consists of mostly ground up meat of some kind and fat. It's a great survival food, and it lasts a long time."

"I think I'll pass on that," said Thomas.

"Me too," said Kinley.

Grandpa continued, "The flying went well, but they were going against a heavy wind from the storm, and it definitely was getting darker and darker. They were flying along until 9:02 p.m.—when it happened."

"They ran out of gas?" Thomas guessed.

"No," said Grandpa, "the engine just stopped. Now they had a big problem, but thankfully, Carl Ben was the pilot. He had been in situations like this before ... well, maybe not quite as bad as *this*. The next several minutes must have been unbelievably scary. Carl Ben was essentially trying to glide a plane—in the dark—and land it on an unknown surface—which hopefully *wouldn't* be the ocean!"

"Yikes!" Kinley exclaimed.

CHAPTER 21

125 Miles to Safety

"What happened, Grandpa!?" Kinley asked nervously.

"With God's help, they landed safely," said Grandpa. "Miraculously, they actually landed on snow in the dark. It was a little rough, and they bounced before landing on the snow, but they landed and came to a stop and they were okay. Then both Carl Ben and Wilkins did something that you might find a little strange and unexpected."

"What?" asked Thomas.

"They laughed and laughed, and then they laughed some more," Grandpa replied. "They had gone through all those agonizing minutes as they approached for a landing in the dark, and they both realized how blessed they were to still be alive."

"I think I would have cried," said Kinley.

"I can't even imagine what I would have done," said Grandpa. "And after that, the two men looked out the windows of the plane into the blizzard conditions around them, and they heard an ominous sound. The large ice pack below them was constantly moving and shifting. They were floating on ice in the middle of nowhere in a blizzard a long way from anyone."

"But they were alive," said Thomas.

"Now what?" asked Kinley.

"Well," said Grandpa, "they were both totally exhausted, and they knew there really wasn't anything they could do right then, so they crawled into their sleeping bags and went to sleep."

"There's no way I could have slept in those conditions," said Thomas.

"But remember, Thomas," said Grandpa, "Carl Ben and Captain Wilkins had slept in adverse conditions many times before, plus they were totally exhausted. But I'm pretty sure sleeping in the cockpit of that airplane after what they'd gone through wasn't as comfortable as you two sleeping in your beds. There were probably a lot of thoughts going through their minds. And when they woke up the next day, they got a good handle on their situation. On the positive side, they noticed the landing was definitely a miracle. Carl Ben had landed the plane on a small pan of ice only about 90 feet by 45 feet in blizzard conditions with no gas."

"In the dark," Thomas added.

"That's right," said Grandpa. "And they were both unhurt. They had a shortwave radio, but it was probably out of range of anyone, but they continued to try to send messages anyway. They had some instruments available, so they could determine exactly where they were—65 miles northwest of Barrow. Unfortunately, they were moving constantly on their chunk of ice farther and farther from where they wanted to go. Probably the best thing of all was the fact that these two guys had already been through a lot of really challenging experiences in their lives, and they weren't likely to panic. If anyone could get back to safety, it was those two."

"What did they have to eat?" asked Kinley.

"They had that pemmican we talked about, some raisins, chocolate, biscuits, and malted milk tablets. They had thermos bottles, so they could put ice in them and then melt the ice in their sleeping bags. They also had rifles and ammunition in case they found any game along the way. They were even able to make a stove out of a tin can, and they used oil they drained from the plane as fuel. But they had a huge problem right off the bat. The blizzard lasted five more days. … Just imagine being stuck in that plane for five days! Ben had trouble sleeping because of the pain from the frostbite on his fingers. The little finger on his right hand was actually turning black, so they knew they really needed to get back to a doctor as quickly as possible."

"And they do it, don't they?" Kinley asked.

"Yes, they do," said Grandpa. "It's beyond amazing how they get back! You two know how tough it is to walk around in cold blizzard conditions with deep snow and stuff. The three of us have done that together for fun, but we usually only do it for 20 minutes or so in the neighborhood, and we can get back to a warm house whenever we get cold. Carl Ben and Captain Wilkins ended up traveling 125 miles in 13 days to get to safety under much worse conditions than we ever come up against. I can't even imagine what they did, traveling all those miles through snow and over high ridges of ice and huge cracks or crevices. Many times, they had to crawl over the ice because it was so thin. They knew they would be in huge trouble if they ever fell through the ice."

"What if there was open water between the ice chunks?" asked Thomas.

"That actually happened to them several times," said Grandpa. "Sometimes they could find a small chunk of ice to get on and use their snowshoes to paddle across the water. But sometimes that wasn't possible, so they had to make a raft out of some sealskin bags called *pokes*. They would inflate the pokes, make a raft, and float across the open water."

Kinley said, "Grandpa, please tell us more about their journey from the beginning. I'll bet they had some close calls, didn't they?"

"I'll tell you what," said Grandpa. "I'll try to give you a good idea of what happened during those 13 days, and when I'm done, maybe we should go outside and try to experience a little of what *they* experienced."

"That's a great idea, Grandpa," said Kinley.

"I can't wait!" said Thomas.

Grandpa said, "Let's check to see what it's like outside now."

Kinley and Thomas could see the snow blowing past the windows as they followed Grandpa to the front door. Grandpa opened the door, and they could see and feel the conditions as the approaching blizzard was beginning to show itself in a big way. The snow was blowing around, with small drifts already forming. The temperature was cold, but still in a moderate 20-degree range."

Grandpa closed the door. "We'll definitely have some fun out there," he said.

They returned to the kitchen table, and Grandpa continued telling the story. "So, Carl Ben and Wilkins left the plane on April 3, 1927. Before they took off, they wrote all the details of the flight they'd made on the ceiling inside the plane, just in case someone might find it. They sent a last message on the radio, and then they got everything ready for their journey. They put their supplies on two sleds they had built out of parts from the plane, and then they took off. Ben followed behind Wilkins, each of them pulling their sled. … Well, the first day was extremely tough, with windy conditions and lots of snow drifts they had to pull their loaded sleds over. It was *really* slow going. After five exhausting hours, they did what they would do after each hard day of their journey—they built an igloo. Wilkins knew exactly how to cut the chunks of snow with the double-edged saw they had, and then they formed them into the igloo. They thawed out a little food on their stove, and after they ate, they went to sleep. From what I read, with the igloo and the reindeer skin sleeping bags placed on a layer of snowshoes and sealskin pokes and other stuff, it was quite comfortable for them. But Wilkins definitely slept better than Carl Ben did that first night."

"Because of Carl Ben's fingers?" Kinley guessed.

"That's right," said Grandpa. "But Carl Ben got some sleep. The second day was a lot like the first, but on the morning of the third day, Wilkins had a couple of suggestions. First, he thought they should change into some Inuit clothes they had brought along, and second, they should discard their old clothes and some other things and use just one sled so they could make more progress."

"What did they keep?" asked Thomas.

"Food, of course," said Grandpa, "plus the stove, the camera Wilkins had along, one sleeping bag, the rifles and ammunition, and some scientific equipment. The ideas of changing into Inuit clothes and just using one sled worked out well for them. Both men felt more comfortable in the Inuit clothes, and now they could take turns with the sled and make better progress. That afternoon, though, they had a pretty big challenge—crossing open water for the first time."

"Oh no," Kinley said, wincing.

"Don't worry, Kinley," said Grandpa. "They got lucky. Wilkins spotted some cakes of ice that spanned the open water, but they had to be very careful crossing them. Wilkins went first, pulling the sled. He seemed to have no problem crossing, probably because he had done stuff like that before. Carl Ben went next, crossing a little more awkwardly, but he made it. ... Then something very strange happened. Carl Ben thought he saw an upside-down mountain in front of them."

"Was he seeing things?" Thomas guessed.

"It was a mirage," said Grandpa. "Apparently, this was something Wilkins had heard about happening in the Arctic, but he had never experienced it before."

"What exactly is a *mirage* and what causes it?" asked Kinley.

"That's a good question, Kinley," said Grandpa. "I've always thought of it as an optical illusion connected to severe heat conditions in desert regions, but never with severe cold. We can research that later. ... As the days went by, you can imagine what a challenge each day must have been for the two men. Eventually, they got rid of the sled and carried what they had in backpacks. As they were slowly moving all those difficult, painful miles, you know what really helped get Carl Ben through, despite all the pain he was experiencing?"

"I'm guessing his strong will," said Thomas.

"The strong friendship he had with Wilkins?" said Kinley.

"Both of those were definitely important," said Grandpa. "And something else that helped Carl Ben immensely was him thinking of his wonderful mother reading Bible verses to him when he was growing up. Thinking of many of those verses and repeating them over and over in his mind brought tremendous strength and comfort to Carl Ben. He also thought of some of the poetry that he had taught his students in Fairbanks."

"Grandpa, did Carl Ben and Captain Wilkins ever get into really big trouble?" Thomas asked.

"There were a lot of precarious situations," said Grandpa.

"What does *precarious* mean again?" asked Kinley.

"It means *dangerous*, *perilous*, or *risky*," said Grandpa. "And those situations must have been especially precarious and challenging for Carl Ben, because whenever he had to use his hands, it must have hurt him a lot. There was one precarious situation I'll tell you about, then let's go outside for a while."

"Awesome!" said Thomas.

"So," Grandpa began, "this was toward the end of the 13 days. They knew they were getting close to land, and they even saw seals for the first time. Anyway, they needed to cross about 50 feet of thin ice to get where they wanted to go. Carl Ben tested the ice, and he broke through, but he was able to get to safety without falling in and getting wet. Captain Wilkins found a better place to cross the ice, and he crossed it carefully with his ice pick in hand. After that, he called to Carl Ben to come across … and then it happened! The ice all around Wilkins started cracking, and before he could do anything, he went into the water. He rolled over, came up, sank, and rolled over some more. Somehow, Wilkins was able to use that ice pick in his hands to grab onto some solid ice and get to the surface and then up on the top of the ice."

"It wouldn't take long to freeze to death when you're soaked," said Kinley.

"That's right," said Grandpa, "and it was so fortunate he knew exactly what to do. Moving and dancing to keep up circulation, he rubbed his clothing with snow to get out most of the water. … Now it was Carl Ben's turn to try to cross the ice. Wilkins managed to get a rope out of his backpack, and he threw it over to Carl Ben. Then Carl Ben took his backpack off, attached the rope to it, and Wilkins pulled it over. With that weight off his back, Carl Ben was able to cross the ice safely. After that, Carl Ben helped Wilkins quickly pull off his socks and mukluks, and the wet socks were replaced with dry ones."

"It gives me the chills just thinking about it," said Kinley.

CHAPTER 22

The Blizzard Hike

Grandpa, Kinley, and Thomas went out to the heated garage to get ready to go outside into the near-blizzard conditions.

Grandpa said, "This experience should give us a little feel for what Carl Ben and Captain Wilkins went through for 13 days. But remember, we're only going out there for about 15 minutes."

"So," Kinley said, "Carl Ben and Captain Wilkins' journey would have been about how many times longer than ours is going to be?"

"Comparing 13 days to 15 minutes—that will be an excellent math problem for us after we get back in," said Grandpa. "Right now, though, let's do a few things to make this experience as realistic as we can."

"We need to be pulling our sleds through the blizzard, right?" said Thomas.

"Yeah," added Kinley, "and we need to put some extra weight on them too."

"We can do that," said Grandpa. "Why don't you each take a sled off the hooks on the wall over there. I'll get some elastic cords out of a drawer, and we can attach some stuff to the sleds to add weight. We can use some of my weights that I use for weightlifting and put them in a backpack or something and attach them to the sleds."

Kinley asked, "Aren't you going to get a sled, Grandpa?"

"No, I'm going to lead the way for you two like Wilkins or Carl Ben did when they had just one sled," Grandpa replied.

"We need some rope to attach to the sled and put around our waists," said Thomas.

"Yup," said Grandpa. "I'll get that for you."

When they had the sleds, rope, weights, backpacks, and elastic cords ready, Grandpa gave Kinley and Thomas a few instructions as they prepared their sleds for their adventure. Grandpa watched proudly as they used the rope knots that he had taught them to make over the years. After that, they got dressed in their snowmobile suits, gloves, stocking caps, and scarfs. Then they put on their boots and walked to the side door of the garage.

"Here we go!" Kinley said excitedly.

"Think of Carl Ben and Wilkins as we're doing this," said Grandpa.

Grandpa held the door open as Kinley and Thomas pulled their sleds out of the garage. Then Grandpa followed them outside and closed the garage door behind him.

The three adventurers stepped out into a windy winter wonderland. All three of them had big smiles on their faces, as they took off on their trek around the neighborhood. For the next 15 minutes, Grandpa led Kinley and Thomas at a challenging pace. The two grandkids were having a fun time pulling the sleds through the snow and wind, but it was hard work. Grandpa was loving every minute of it.

As they walked past the Ericksons' house, three children waved from their large picture window. Their dog, Bimbo, barked excitedly as he watched along with them. Grandpa, Kinley, and Thomas waved back.

When they got back inside the garage and sat down on a bench, Thomas said, "That was really fun, but I'm exhausted, Grandpa."

"Me too," said Kinley. "That was a blast, but it was really tough. There aren't a lot of people in the world who could have done what Carl Ben and Captain Wilkins did for 13 days."

"Grandpa," said Thomas, "please tell us what it was like when they finally got to safety."

"Okay," said Grandpa. "It was April 16, and they'd traveled those 125 miles in 13 days, and they finally got off the moving ice and onto land at the coast of Alaska. Not too long after that, they saw tracks from a sled, and then they saw the Trading Post at Beechey Point in the distance."

"I'll bet they celebrated," said Kinley.

"It must have been such a great feeling," said Grandpa. "Carl Ben and Wilkins hadn't talked much all those days because they were saving energy for their incredible ordeal, but now they chattered away like crazy. Not too long after that, two dog teams came toward them as they were walking toward the Trading Post."

Thomas asked, "Had anyone been looking for Carl

Ben and Wilkins?"

"Yes," said Grandpa. "Alger Graham had been flying the *Detroit News Number 2* all around the area looking for the two men for several days. He had even flown over Inuit settlements and Beechey Point and dropped messages on paper down from his plane asking the people to look out for them. By this time, almost everyone must have figured Carl Ben and Wilkins were dead. But Alger Graham wasn't about to give up. He figured if anyone could survive, it would be those two."

"And he was right," said Kinley.

"Yes, he was," said Grandpa.

"Did Carl Ben lose that little finger?" asked Thomas.

"Yes, he did," said Grandpa. "As soon as Alger Graham picked them up in the airplane, he took them to Barrow and the doctor there amputated his little finger. … And that was the end of any significant exploration for that year. I think Carl Ben and Wilkins must have wondered if they would ever get a chance to fly together the next year, but they did. And you won't believe what happened. It just gets more and more amazing!"

Kinley grimaced. "Please tell me there were no more 13-day hikes."

"No, there weren't," said Grandpa, chuckling. "But I can't wait to tell you about what happened next. Right now, though, let's have some more hot chocolate, then we can work on that math problem we talked about—no calculators allowed."

CHAPTER 23

It's a Long Way to Spitsbergen

Grandpa said, "What Carl Ben and Captain Wilkins did that next year, 1928, is really hard to believe. In fact, pretty much everyone but those two men thought it was impossible."

"Why?" asked Kinley.

"Because people who had done really tough things themselves, as well as people with common sense, realized how crazy it was to even *attempt* what they were about to attempt. Carl Ben and Captain Wilkins were going to try to fly nonstop from Barrow to an island in Europe 2,200 miles away called Spitsbergen. To get there, they would fly on a course that was isolated and barren and unforgiving, mostly over the Arctic Ocean, and there were very few landmarks along the way to help with navigation. If they were forced to land at *any* time for *any* reason, they most likely wouldn't be found for months or even years if they were ever found at all. … Let me show you a map of the 2,200-mile route they would eventually take."

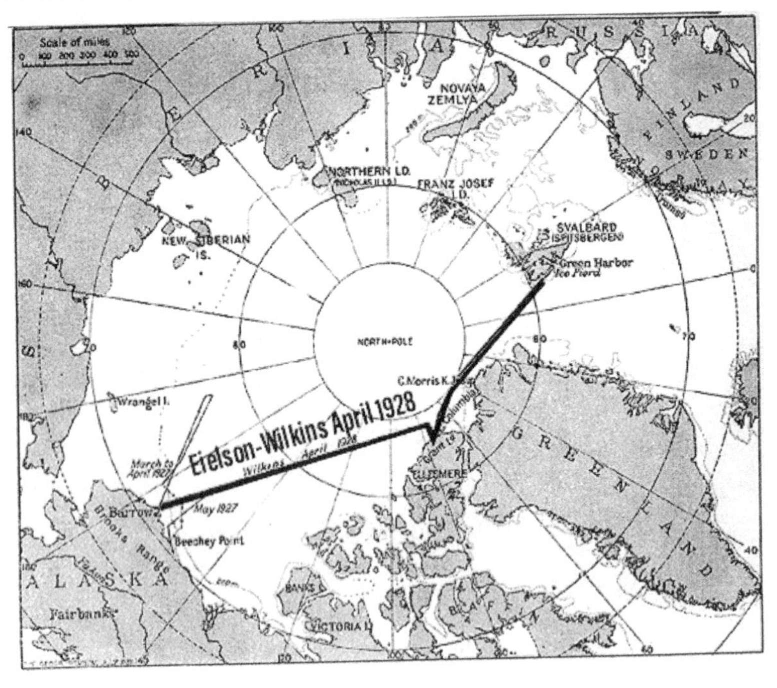

WILKINS-EIELSON FLIGHTS, 1927 AND 1928, INCLUDING THE 13-DAY TREK TO BEECHEY POINT; *SMITHSONIAN INSTITUTION*

Grandpa showed them the map of the journey on his computer.

"What country is Spitsbergen part of?" asked Thomas.

Grandpa pointed to Spitsbergen on the map and said, "Spitsbergen is the largest island in this group of islands. It's part of Norway, about 600 miles north of the tip of that country. ... Now, I'll give either one of you a dollar if you can give me the fancy name for a group of islands."

"Archipelago," Kinley answered immediately. "We studied that last month in school. I can spell it too—a-r-c-h-i-p-e-l-a-g-o."

"You're amazing, Kinley!" said Grandpa. "The

archipelago that Spitsbergen is part of is called *Svalbard* (svahl-bahr)."

Thomas asked, "How many islands are there in Svalbard?"

"Nine major ones," Grandpa answered. "I'm not sure how many islands altogether, but I do know that most of the population of the archipelago is in Spitsbergen."

"Carl Ben's ancestors were from Norway, right?" asked Kinley.

"That's right," said Grandpa. "So, flying there must have been extra cool for him. But, as you two might expect, there were a lot of hurdles to jump before the flight to Spitsbergen would even get off the ground."

"And some crashes and stuff too, I'll bet," Kinley guessed.

Grandpa chuckled. "No real major ones. But one of the first big problems was—Wilkins couldn't find anyone who would financially support their venture, so he had to sell his other planes and finance it all by himself."

"Why wasn't anyone interested?" asked Thomas.

Grandpa explained, "Carl Ben and Wilkins may have done some pretty amazing things the past two years, but they really hadn't achieved enough to get a lot of people excited, and this next venture was a long shot and wasn't likely to succeed. Really, why would anyone want to put their money into something that was likely to fail? But you know Wilkins. That wasn't going to stop *him*. He sold his planes and found a new plane in California called a Lockheed Vega monoplane that he saw flying in San Francisco one day. He thought it would be perfect for their flight to Spitsbergen. Then he had the Lockheed

Company build a special Vega plane with extra gas tanks so they could fly the entire 2,200 miles. He also had them install windows on the floor to help him with his navigation. The plane was given the name *Detroit News* in honor of all the help they'd received from the people from Detroit, and then Wilkins had the words *Wilkins Arctic Expedition* painted in large letters on the side."

THE DETROIT NEWS WITH CARL BEN ON THE RIGHT AND AN UNIDENTIFIED MAN ON THE LEFT; *STATE HISTORICAL SOCIETY OF NORTH DAKOTA*

"What was Carl Ben doing all this time?" asked Thomas.

"He had a new job with the United States Government that really never existed before this," said Grandpa. "He flew around inspecting airplanes, pilots, and new airfields in the United States. But as soon as Wilkins contacted him about getting the new plane that he wanted tested for their flight to Spitsbergen, Carl Ben got leave from that job and headed out to California to test out the new plane. And boy, did he give it a test!"

"But he didn't wreck it, right?" asked Kinley.

"Only once, when the engine didn't work right," Grandpa answered, "but it didn't do any significant damage when he had to make a rough landing. There were some kinks to work out with the engine, but they got that done. Carl Ben and Captain Wilkins flew the plane several times a day for weeks, and both men got to like the plane more and more as they kept flying. By the time they were done, they both had confidence the plane would work well in the extreme cold conditions they'd be flying in. … Then, on February 3, Wilkins arranged for the plane to be shipped to Fairbanks, and Carl Ben went to Seattle to spend some time with his dad and Elma."

"What did his dad say to him this time?" asked Kinley.

"I think he had given up trying to talk Carl Ben out of flying," said Grandpa, "but you can imagine how worried both Ole and Elma were."

Thomas said, "It must have been tough saying good-bye after their visit."

"That's for sure," said Grandpa. "Carl Ben and Wilkins got to Fairbanks on February 26, and there weren't a lot of people interested in what they were going to attempt as they prepared for it. On March 19, they said good-bye to friends before they took off for Barrow."

"Was Marie Banks there?" asked Kinley.

"Yes, she was," Grandpa replied. "Carl Ben promised her that he would return, but I'm not so sure even Marie was convinced that was likely to happen. Neither did most of his friends."

"Yeah, look what happened last year," said Thomas. "And this was much more dangerous."

"Anyway," said Grandpa, "once they got to Barrow, they had plenty to do there before they could fly to Spitsbergen."

"Did they pack a lot of survival stuff?" asked Kinley.

"They sure did," said Grandpa. "And they had plenty of experience from the past year to know what worked and what didn't work. They had the right equipment to survive months if they had to. They even had surgical instruments and more medical supplies in case they were needed."

Thomas asked, "Grandpa, what do you think turned out to be the most challenging part of the flight to Spitsbergen?"

"That's a great question," said Grandpa. "Probably just getting their plane off the ground at the start."

"Why?" asked Kinley.

"Just picture this," said Grandpa. "You've got a plane that weighs about 2,000 pounds, then you add about 3,500 pounds of gasoline, equipment, and supplies onboard. Now, you need a runway cut through ice and snow that's wide enough and long enough so you can get up enough speed to take off."

"Yikes," said Thomas. "How long does the runway have to be?"

"They found that out the hard way," said Grandpa. "On April 7, their first runway was too short, and they damaged one of the metal skis trying to take off. Then they tried again after they replaced the metal skis with wooden ones, and they failed again, but no damage was done this time. However, they realized they needed a longer runway. The problem was, they had to move the plane five miles away and then shovel and clear another runway there."

"Who helped them with all that work?" asked Kinley.

"Ten Inuit men and 25 dogs towed the plane those five miles, and more than 30 Inuit men helped clear and shovel the new runway."

"How long was it? asked Thomas.

"About a mile," Grandpa replied. "They were ready to try again on April 15, and this time they got off the ground."

"What a relief!" said Kinley.

"It sure was," said Grandpa. "And I can't even imagine how incredible it must have been as they were flying over territory that no one had ever seen before on a trip that almost no one thought was possible. Wilkins had to use all his skill in navigation and Carl Ben had to use all his flying skill for almost a whole day flying nonstop. There were mountains, awful weather conditions, storms, and 50 below zero temperatures to make it even more challenging. There really wasn't any room for error."

"How long were they actually in the air?" asked Thomas.

"Twenty hours and twenty minutes total," answered Grandpa. "Carl Ben noticed that, if anything did go wrong, there was no place to land. There were no areas of smooth ice large enough to land on down below, and even if they did land, with all that weight, they wouldn't be able to take off again. On the positive side, though, the engine sounded good from the start."

"It must have been *so* exciting," said Kinley.

"I can feel it in my stomach just thinking about it," said Grandpa. "As they were approaching Greenland, Wilkins handed Carl Ben a note informing him there was a storm over the island. They had to make a choice whether to land or go on. Carl Ben chose to go on, and Wilkins agreed. That made the last part of their trip extra challenging. Carl Ben couldn't get the plane high enough to escape the clouds, winds, and sheets of rain. The plane was tossed around, with the swirling snow forcing Carl Ben to fly almost blind. Wilkins had him drop down and fly at a low altitude, hoping to find a safe place to land. Finally, they spotted one, and Carl Ben was able to land safely. Wilkins handed Carl Ben a note—*We are in Spitsbergen*!"

"Hooray!" Thomas yelled, fist-bumping Grandpa and Kinley.

CHAPTER 24

Time to Celebrate

"What a great feeling that must have been!" Kinley exclaimed.

"Tremendous!" added Grandpa. "Unfortunately, they had landed in Spitsbergen during a terrible blizzard, and they didn't know exactly where they were, so they were in some real danger."

"Nothing comes easily for Carl Ben and Wilkins, does it?" said Thomas.

"You can say that again," said Grandpa, chuckling. "Thank goodness the plane wasn't damaged, so they immediately covered the engine and drained the oil, plus they compacted the snow around the skis so the plane wouldn't flip over in the wind. They had about 20 gallons of gasoline left, and they figured that would be enough to get them to a town nearby if they could get back up in the air. Wilkins was pretty sure they were close to a place called Green Harbour."

"How long did the blizzard last?" asked Kinley.

"This is pretty amazing," said Grandpa. "They landed at 6:35 p.m. on Monday, April 16, 1928, but they wouldn't get into the air again until Saturday. Wilkins said the blizzard was the worst he'd ever experienced in the Arctic—and that's saying something."

"I'll bet they had some serious shoveling to do on Saturday before they could take off," said Kinley.

"That's right," said Grandpa. "They didn't have any help from the Inuit this time either. Thank goodness, much of the weight was gone from the plane now because they'd used up all that fuel, so they could get off the ground without such a long runway. Six hours of shoveling would do the trick, but they had another problem."

"A polar bear blocked the runway?" Kinley guessed, giggling.

"Not quite," said Grandpa with a chuckle. "When Carl Ben powered up, the plane didn't move at all, so it needed a little push. That meant Wilkins would have to push off somehow and then get back in the plane."

"I'll bet it didn't work the first time," said Thomas. "Nothing seems to work the first time for these two guys."

"You're right," said Grandpa. "The first time Wilkins pushed off and tried to hop back into the cabin, but he wasn't able to get back in the plane. Carl Ben realized that Wilkins wasn't in the plane after he took off, so he turned around and landed to pick him up."

"Now they had even less gas," Kinley noted.

"That's right," said Grandpa. "Plus, Carl Ben was worried about the skis breaking if they had to land another time. That would *really* be a problem! … So, the second time, Wilkins tried to push off and then grab onto a rope ladder that was dangling out of the cabin so he could pull himself into the plane."

"It didn't work, did it?" Thomas guessed.

"Nope," said Grandpa. "Wilkins tried to grab the ladder after pushing off, then he jerked off his mittens to get a better grip, but his fingers got so cold, he couldn't hold on anymore. So, then he tried to grasp it with his teeth—"

"No way!" Kinley exclaimed.

"He tried but he couldn't hold on with his teeth," said Grandpa. "He had to let go—then to make it even worse, he got hit by the tail of the plane."

"Yikes!' Thomas exclaimed. "Please tell me the third time is a charm."

"Yes! Please, Grandpa," Kinley pleaded.

"Okay, the third time *was* a charm," said Grandpa, smiling. "That time they found a piece of driftwood that Wilkins could use as a pole, and he pushed off while leaning out of the cabin, using a rowing motion. It worked. Carl Ben took off, and he got the plane up to about 3,000 feet. From up there, they almost immediately spotted some houses with antennas mounted on two radio masts."

"Please land the plane safely, Carl Ben!" Kinley exclaimed.

"Don't worry, he did," said Grandpa. "And then it didn't take long for a young girl and four men to spot them and ski out to meet them. One of the men greeted Carl Ben and Wilkins in Norwegian, and Carl Ben used the best Norwegian he could remember to answer. Then he explained who they were and where they had come from. The four men and the girl were amazed at what they heard about the flight that Carl Ben and Wilkins had just completed."

"Did they help spread the news to everyone?" asked Thomas.

"Yes," said Grandpa, "it didn't take long before they all realized that they all spoke English, so communication got much better. One of the men named Bowitz Ihlen was the manager of the Government Radio Station nearby. Two of the other men were telegraphers. They used their telegraph and radio to help get the word out about the incredible flight of Carl Ben and Wilkins."

"Did they contact Carl Ben's family?" asked Kinley.

"Yes," said Grandpa, "Carl Ben sent out a message that they'd arrived safely—and that he would see them soon."

"I'll bet they *really* celebrated after that," said Thomas.

"It was pretty awesome," said Grandpa. "It made any Super Bowl celebration look like small potatoes. The first celebration was at Bowitz Ihlen's house, but after that, it seemed like practically everyone in the world wanted to get involved in honoring Carl Ben and Wilkins."

"Where did they go after they left Spitsbergen?" asked Kinley.

"The celebrations continued there in Norway," said Grandpa, "and you can bet those Norwegians were particularly proud to honor someone like Carl Ben, who had Norwegian blood in him. Then there were big celebrations in the Norwegian cities of Tromso, Bergen, and Oslo. In Oslo, Carl Ben and Wilkins were awarded special medals by Roald Amundsen who declared the flight the most important flight *ever* over unexplored Arctic Territory."

"And that's saying a lot coming from a guy like Roald Amundsen," said Thomas.

"Yes, he was one of the most famous Norwegian explorers *ever*," said Grandpa. "After Norway, the celebrations moved to Copenhagen, Denmark; Berlin, Germany; Amsterdam, Holland; London, England; and Paris, France. There were speeches, celebrations, parades, awards, flowers, kings and queens and princes, movie stars, and lots of gifts. I think Carl Ben said he got about a dozen watches along the way."

"That must have been *so* exciting!" said Kinley.

Grandpa said, "Knowing Carl Ben, it might have been a little difficult for him because he liked to downplay what he'd accomplished with Wilkins. But no matter what, it was an unbelievable experience—traveling the world and meeting lots of interesting people. They finally got a break in late June when they took the ocean liner *Stavangerfjord* to New York City, but when they got there, the celebrations and honors continued."

"What happened in New York?" asked Kinley.

"They got there on July 3, and the people in New York were anxious to honor Carl Ben and Wilkins. There was a welcoming tugboat blaring out its sirens with a band on board. Carl Ben's dad and his brother Arthur were on board the tugboat, and other ships joined in the noisy celebration. A ticker tape parade followed, and after that, Carl Ben and Wilkins met many of the most important and famous people in New York City. After New York, there were other cities that wanted to be part of the celebration, too, including Buffalo, Atlantic City,

Detroit, Cleveland, Milwaukee, and Des Moines. Would you believe—it wasn't until July 20, 1928 that Carl Ben and Wilkins got to North Dakota."

"And I'll bet they had a *huge* celebration there," said Kinley.

"It really was," said Grandpa.

"When did they land in Spitsbergen again?" asked Thomas.

"April 16," Kinley answered quickly.

Thomas said, "And they got to North Dakota on July 20. … Wow! That's about 95 days since they landed for celebrations and stuff. That *does* make a Super Bowl celebration look like small potatoes!"

Grandpa smiled. "And just wait till you hear what happened when Carl Ben gets back home to Hatton," he said.

CHAPTER 25

The Amazing Hatton Celebration

"What happened in Hatton, Grandpa?" Kinley asked anxiously.

Grandpa replied, "You two know how exciting it is around here on Independence Day in Mandan, right?"

"Of course," said Thomas. "It's the most exciting time of the year."

Kinley said, "I love the parade and the rodeo and Art in the Park and the fun run and and all the food and the thousands of people!"

"And the *huge* fireworks display after the rodeo," Thomas added.

"Yes," said Kinley. "How could I forget that?"

"Well," said Grandpa, "the Hatton celebration for Carl Ben and Wilkins had a parade, lots of food, lots of entertainment, and lots of fun, just like our Mandan Independence Day celebration. There was no rodeo, but there were some pretty amazing aerial circuses."

"How about fireworks?" asked Thomas.

"I don't think there were fireworks," said Grandpa. "But Carl Ben must have had two days that were more spectacular than any fireworks display, and he got to share them with his closest family and friends. … It all began on the morning of July 20 when Carl Ben flew the Vega airplane, Wilkins onboard, from Milwaukee to Fargo. This just happened to be Carl Ben's thirty-first birthday. When they got to Fargo, Carl Ben circled Hector Airport three times as a salute, and then he landed the plane at about 4:00 in the afternoon. Carl Ben and Wilkins got a huge heroes' welcome in Fargo from lots of friends, family, and others, and there was a dinner party birthday celebration later—but what was waiting in Hatton the next day was *really* something special!"

"I can't wait," said Kinley.

Grandpa said, "Early the next day, Saturday morning, Carl Ben got word that he was to land on Thorval Staven's field in Hatton—just like old times. Carl Ben and Wilkins flew from Fargo to Hatton that morning, not having any idea what the townspeople of Hatton had planned for them. If Carl Ben thought he was going to have lots of time to relax at home and enjoy some downtime, he would soon find out—that wasn't going to happen. As they approached Hatton, they got quite a sight from the air."

"Thousands of people," Thomas guessed.

"That's right," said Grandpa. "The local newspaper described it as more than 5,000 people. It was a huge crowd. After Carl Ben landed the plane, Carl Ben and Wilkins made their way through the crowd, and everyone wanted to shake their hands and congratulate them. Carl Ben was overwhelmed at all the people who had shown up to greet him. So many of them were familiar faces from his time growing up in Hatton."

Plane landing in Hatton; *State Historical Society of North Dakota*

"Was Marie Banks there?" asked Kinley.

"I couldn't find any information about that, but I'm sure she was," Grandpa answered. "Anyway, after that, there was a big parade with over 800 people and 300 children, then the crowd gathered at the ballpark to honor their hometown hero. Carl Ben and Wilkins were seated at the bandstand, and there were several speeches by prominent people. Then the governor of North Dakota, Governor Sorlie, presented Carl Ben a beautiful gold medal."

"That is so cool!" said Kinley.

"Then I'll bet Carl Ben had to make a speech," said Thomas.

"You're way too smart," said Grandpa, smiling. "Yes, he did. And despite all of Carl Ben's experiences with debate and making speeches all over the world, this was a tough speech for him to get started. He looked out at all the special people who were there in front of him, and he was actually silent for a short time."

Carl Ben in his homecoming parade; *North Dakota State University Archives*

Carl Ben speaks to the crowd in Hatton; *North Dakota State University Archives*

"I've got tears in my eyes just thinking about it," said Kinley.

"Me too," said Grandpa. "Then Carl Ben saw his

debate teacher in the front row, and he regained his composure. He told himself that he'd better do a good job speaking."

"What did Carl Ben say?" asked Thomas.

"Well," said Grandpa, "he was humble, just like you would expect. He downplayed the significance of what he had done, telling the huge audience that *twenty-and-a-half hours of flying and two meals* was hardly deserving of all the praise he was getting. Then he talked about some of the other great explorers who had endured so much exploring the northern polar region. After that, Wilkins spoke and praised Carl Ben and his accomplishments as a pilot and a partner on their venture, and then there was a huge aerial circus."

"Carl Ben must have thought about the time he performed all those stunts in the same place," said Thomas.

"He did," said Grandpa. "Carl Ben also looked over at his dad several times and noticed how relaxed he was and how much fun he seemed to be having."

Kinley said, "A lot different than when Carl Ben was doing the flying."

"It sure was," said Grandpa. "After that, there was an open house at the Eielson home, where Elma, Helen, Hannah, and Adeline worked hard serving people snacks and drinks. Around town there was a real carnival-like atmosphere. That evening there was a banquet where a bunch of speakers who had something to do with flying spoke about how important Carl Ben had been to aviation in North Dakota and the world.

"The next day, on Sunday, Carl Ben finally got a chance to relax in church, but that wouldn't be the end of the celebration. There were more activities to come, including baseball games and another aerial circus."

CHAPTER 26

The Antarctic Expedition

"What did Carl Ben do next, Grandpa?" asked Kinley.

"Well, it sure didn't take him long to get involved in another big adventure," Grandpa replied. "Carl Ben decided to join the Antarctic expedition Wilkins had planned. Carl Ben had a few weeks to relax at home in Hatton before he informed Wilkins in early August that he wanted to join him."

"What's the difference between *Antarctic* and *Antarctica* again?" asked Thomas.

"I know," Kinley answered. "*Antarctica* is the name of the continent and *Antarctic* refers to the whole region."

"Oh," said Thomas.

"How big is the continent of Antarctica, Grandpa?" asked Kinley.

"It's huge," said Grandpa. "You could fit about 78 North Dakotas into it. Another way to look at it, it's about the size of the United States and Mexico combined."

"Wow!" Thomas exclaimed.

Kinley said, "And I read that it's covered by ice that's

three miles thick in some places."

"Three miles!" Thomas exclaimed. "I can't even imagine ice that thick."

Kinley said, "And Carl Ben and Wilkins flying over both the Arctic and Antarctica in one year! I'll bet that will be a record—if they actually do it."

"Let's not jump too far ahead in the story," said Grandpa, smiling. "By September 21, Carl Ben was in New York City with Wilkins, and they were ready to begin their next adventure. A photographer even took a photo of Carl Ben standing on his head—representing the fact that he would soon be at the *bottom* of the globe."

"I'd love to see that photo," said Kinley, laughing.

"Me too," Thomas added.

Grandpa said, "That's something else we can look for later."

"Did Carl Ben and Wilkins have better support for this expedition?" asked Thomas.

"That's a good question," said Grandpa. "It was a lot easier for Wilkins to get good financial backing this time because of the success they had on their flight to Spitsbergen. He was even able to purchase another new Lockheed Vega. The other key people on the expedition were Joe Crosson, who was Carl Ben's good friend and also the second pilot; Orval Porter, the mechanic; and a radio operator named William Gaston."

"How long did it take them to get to the Antarctic?" asked Kinley.

"Kinley, please go get my globe in my study so we can trace their route," said Grandpa.

Kinley ran and got the globe and returned.

Grandpa pointed to New York City on the globe. "I think it's between nine or ten thousand miles if you could fly from New York City to Antarctica the most direct route, but they were going there by ship, with their two planes strapped to the boat. There was the Vega they used on their flight to Spitsbergen which they called the *Los Angeles*, and then there was the new Vega they called the *San Francisco*. … So, Kinley, point at New York City on the globe. … Now, please point at Antarctica. … Just imagine this. They left New York on September 22, 1928, and they didn't get to their base of operations in the Antarctic called Deception Island until November 8."

Thomas thought for several seconds. "Wow!" he said. "It took them about 47 days. That's a long trip."

"Kinley can trace the trip they took," said Grandpa. "First, they took an ocean liner named the *Southern Cross* from New York City to Montevideo, Uruguay, and arrived there on October 10—but they had to wait there for 13 days to board another ship, a whaling ship called the *Hektoria*, which would take them the rest of the way."

The *Hektoria*; Author's Collection

"About a month has gone by already," said Thomas. "I wonder what Carl Ben and everyone did to keep busy all that time."

"Carl Ben mentioned that he did lots of reading," said Grandpa, "and there was also a lot of time spent just sharing stories from their lives."

"I'd love to see a list of the books he read," said Kinley.

Thomas giggled. "I'll bet there weren't any of those old Bobbsey Twins and Nancy Drew books that Great-Grandma gave you on that list," he said.

"You never know, Thomas," said Grandpa, chuckling. "I've enjoyed some of those old Nancy Drew books myself. … Anyway, after they got onboard the *Hektoria* in Montevideo, it was about 16 more days until they got to a bay on Deception Island, which is part of the Shetland Islands near the Antarctic Peninsula. The *Hektoria* anchored there, and that's where Carl Ben and the rest of the men stayed during the expedition."

"How did it get a name like Deception Island?" asked Thomas. "Was there something deceiving about the island?"

"There sure was," Grandpa answered. "The island appeared to be a normal island, but it was actually a ring around a flooded *caldera*, a volcanic crater that was formed when the volcano erupted. And the volcano was still active!"

"Please tell me the volcano doesn't erupt while Carl Ben is there," said Kinley.

"It doesn't," Grandpa assured her.

"Grandpa," asked Thomas, "what exactly did they want to accomplish on this expedition?"

"Wilkins wanted to explore and map some territory along the Weddell Sea from the air plus do some studies

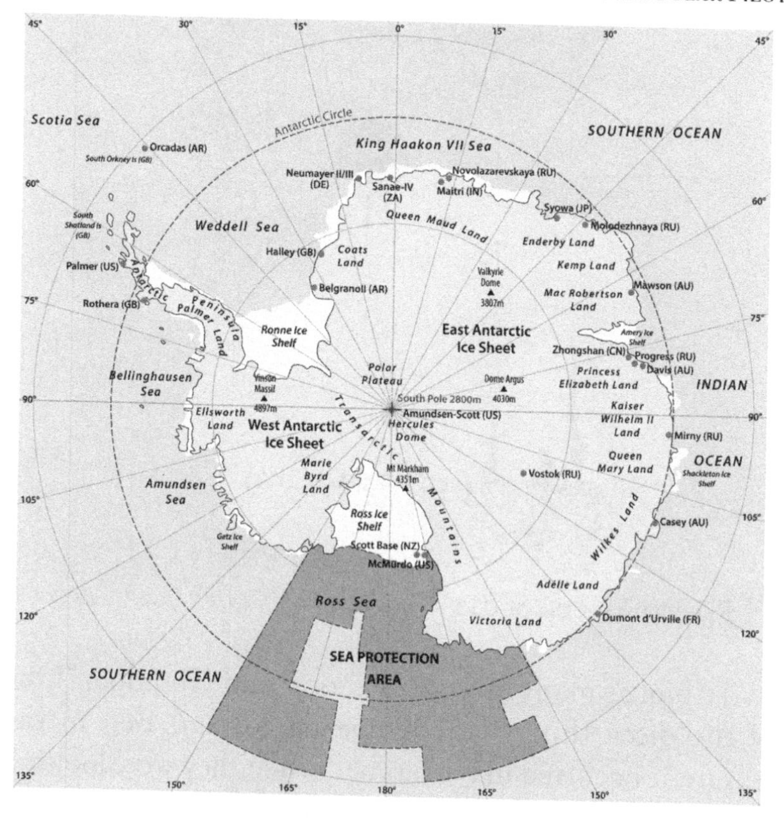

of the weather," said Grandpa. "And how cool would it be—they would be the *first* to fly over both of the polar regions in one year. Plus, if it worked out, Carl Ben could be the *first* to fly a plane on the continent of Antarctica."

Kinley asked, "Had someone already flown a balloon or something over Antarctica?"

"Good guess, Kinley," said Grandpa. "In 1902, a British guy named Robert Falcon Scott flew over Antarctica in a hydrogen balloon attached to a rope that went up about 250 yards. Then he even took some photos from up there."

Kinley grimaced, "I'll bet Carl Ben and Wilkins and the rest of the group had some big challenges and close calls and stuff, didn't they?"

Robert Falcon Scott's Balloon; *Author's Collection*

"Not as many as in the Arctic," said Grandpa. "One of the dicey things that happened to Carl Ben in the Antarctic occurred in November, when they were looking for places to build a landing field. One day when the weather conditions were great, Carl Ben decided to take the *San Francisco* up, then he planned to land on the ice with wheels and put skis on the plane. Unfortunately, when he landed, things went a little whacky. The plane slid about 300 yards—much farther than he wanted it to—onto some ice that was too thin."

"And the plane sunk?" Kinley guessed.

"It did," said Grandpa, "but fortunately, the wings stopped it from sinking totally. Carl Ben got wet, and it took a bunch of the crew from the *Hektoria* about 20 hours to get the plane out. It could have been much worse, but as it turned out, Carl Ben just needed some dry clothes after it happened."

Thomas asked, "What were some of their other biggest challenges and stuff?"

"The weather might have been their biggest challenge," answered Grandpa. "Once they got there, thick foggy conditions settled in, making it impossible to fly, so they had to wait around a lot. And time really wasn't on their side. The best flying weather would run out by early 1929, which didn't give them much time."

Kinley said, "So there was a lot of time waiting for the right weather. I hope Carl Ben still had some books left to read."

Grandpa said, "Carl Ben mentioned the fact that they had really nice quarters onboard the *Hektoria*, and he still had a few good books. I guess someone had an accordion, and there were also two phonographs and some records. You can bet the expeditioners and the men on the ship shared more stories. I read that Carl Ben, Joe, and Orval even shaved their heads and let their beards grow. Also, they explored Deception Island, where there were lots of animals they had never seen before. The penguins came right up to the men and sat on their knees. I can show you a photo of that."

"I love that," said Kinley. "They're so cute."

"When did the weather clear?" asked Thomas.

"It cleared around November 22," Grandpa replied. "Carl Ben was finally able to take the first flight in Antarctica. It was a short flight in the *Los Angeles,* taking off from the shore on skis. But they had a bigger problem to solve before they could take the longer flights that they wanted to take."

"What problem?" asked Kinley.

"Figuring out the best place to take off and land for the longer flights," Grandpa replied. "Do you remember how challenging it was to take off for Spitsbergen with all that extra weight from the fuel, supplies, and equipment?"

PLAYING WITH THE PENGUINS; *AUTHOR'S PHOTO, TAKEN AT THE HATTON-EIELSON MUSEUM*

"Yes," replied Thomas.

"Well," said Grandpa, "this time they had prepared the *San Francisco*, on wheels, to take off and land on the land, and they had the other plane, the *Los Angeles,* with pontoons on it, to take off and land on the water."

"Which one worked better?" asked Thomas.

"The land option ended up working better," answered Grandpa. "The loaded plane couldn't take off with the pontoons, plus they had a problem with the huge number of birds getting in the way on the water. One time when Joe Crosson was flying the *Los Angeles*, a big bird flew right into the propeller after it landed, and the plane couldn't take off from the water after that. ... But the challenge presented by trying to take off from the land in the *San Francisco* was building a runway that was long enough and wide enough on the volcanic pumice that made up Deception Island. The runway they ended up making turned out to be pretty weird and funky, but it worked."

"What do you mean, *pretty weird* and *funky*?" asked Kinley.

"The runway they built is pretty hard to describe," said Grandpa, chuckling, "but Carl Ben said it was the weirdest one he had ever used. To take off, he had to go up a hill, then he turned a little and went down the other side, then he climbed another hill before reaching the end for a possible takeoff."

Kinley giggled. "That's definitely weird and funky," she said.

"And *that* worked?" Thomas asked.

"It sure did," said Grandpa. "On December 20, 1928, Carl Ben successfully took off from that runway with Wilkins on board, and they took their longest flight of the Antarctic expedition. The flight covered a total of about 1,200 miles in 10 hours, and it must have been *spectacular*. They saw scenery unlike anything they'd ever seen. There were high peaks, huge cliffs, large crevices, and gigantic glaciers. Along the way, Wilkins chartered several hundred miles of the coast and even named a few geographical features after himself and Carl Ben—they were called Eielson Peninsula and Wilkins Coast. I've got a few photos of Antarctica to show you that will give you an idea of how beautiful that flight must have been."

CHAPTER 27

Carl Ben's Dream Gets Closer

"Did they get do any more flying in Antarctica after that?" asked Kinley.

"Yes," replied Grandpa, "the weather was good enough to fly again on January 10, but this time Joe Crosson and Wilkins were able to fly only about 250 miles in the *Los Angeles.* They were looking for a good place to base their operations the next year, but they didn't find anything during that flight."

"Did Carl Ben decide to go back the next year?" asked Thomas.

"No," Grandpa replied, "he'd made up his mind what he wanted to do next. His dream of starting an Alaskan airline was his next focus."

Kinley asked, "Were there lots of honors and celebrations again when they got back to the United States?"

"There sure were," Grandpa answered, "but maybe it was a little less intense this time. Carl Ben finally got back to Hatton on March 29, and that's when one of the coolest things happened. There were 300 school kids lined up along the train depot platform, and they were just a small part of a *huge* welcoming party. Then the band started playing, and it eventually led a huge crowd that escorted Carl Ben to his home."

"That is so awesome!" said Kinley.

Grandpa said, "It was also pretty cool in early April when Carl Ben went to a get a big award from President Herbert Hoover in Washington, D.C. called the Harmon Trophy. I've got a few photos of Carl Ben with the trophy here someplace."

Grandpa showed them the photos.

CARL BEN AND THE HARMON TROPHY; *LIBRARY OF CONGRESS PHOTO*

President Hoover on the far left, as Carl Ben receives the Harmon Trophy; *Library of Congress Photo*

Grandpa said, "The Harmon trophy was given to the person who achieved the greatest feat in aviation for that year. Right after he left Washington, D.C., Carl Ben went to New York to try to get some support for the company he wanted to start in Alaska for his freight and passenger air service. He went and talked to the leaders of a big company there called The Aviation Corporation."

"Did he get their support?" Thomas asked.

"Yes," said Grandpa, "and I'll bet it didn't hurt at all that Carl Ben was famous—and he'd just come from getting that award from the president."

"That couldn't hurt," said Kinley, giggling.

"After that," said Grandpa, "Carl Ben returned to

Alaska to try to get things going. When he got to Fairbanks, he got quite a surprise. Before his train even got to town, three of his pilot friends buzzed over the train in their planes. Then hundreds of his friends met him at the train station. There was a huge banquet honoring him in Fairbanks after that, and Carl Ben got a chance to present a banner to the American Legion Club—the banner that he'd carried with him on the flight to Spitsbergen. ... By July 23, The Aviation Corporation told Carl Ben that he could begin buying small Alaskan aviation companies to form the large company that he'd dreamed of. By August 8, Carl Ben had purchased several small companies, and he was appointed executive vice president and general manager of the new Alaskan Airways, Incorporated."

"Was Carl Ben going to be a pilot for his company?" asked Kinley.

"No," replied Grandpa. "Carl Ben told his family they didn't have to worry anymore about him getting hurt flying. He was done, except for maybe a fun flight once in a while. He wanted to focus on making Alaskan Airways successful."

"But he flew more than that, didn't he?" Kinley guessed. "And something bad happened."

Grandpa looked at Kinley with a surprised look on his face. "This next part of the story is going to be a little tough for me to tell you. Would you mind if we eat some more of Great Aunt Karol's chocolate chip cookies while I tell you the next part of the story?"

Kinley said, "Are we going to need the Kleenex again, Grandpa?"

"I think so," said Grandpa.

CHAPTER 28

Rescue Flight to Siberia

"Grandpa, please tell us what happened next," said Kinley.

"Okay," said Grandpa, "things were going great for Carl Ben and his new company. The Post Office Department was even considering air mail service for Alaska, which would bring Carl Ben's company a lot more business. Then, in early October of 1929, Carl Ben got word that a ship called the *Nanuk* was frozen in the ice off North Cape in Siberia with 15 passengers on board along with about a million dollars in furs. Carl Ben was contacted, and he was made this offer—if his company could bring the passengers and cargo back safely, it would get $50,000, which would be tremendous for the new company."

Thomas asked, "How much would that be in today's money?"

"A whole lot," Grandpa replied. "I'm estimating about $750,000."

"Wow!" Kinley exclaimed. "But Carl Ben's company

would be saving lives too."

"That's right," said Grandpa, "but it would be an extremely challenging task. Imagine this, only one pilot had ever flown from Alaska to Siberia before this, and he'd done it during March when the flying weather was pretty good. Flying this late in the year would be a whole different matter."

Kinley looked worried. "Why did Carl Ben think he had to be part of this rescue mission?" she asked. "He must have had a bunch of other pilots working for him."

"Well," said Grandpa, "he knew how dangerous it would be, but there were lives in danger, and he was the most experienced pilot of all. Plus, he didn't have a wife and kids like many of the other pilots did."

"Did he tell Marie and his family why he was going to go back on his promise to them?" asked Kinley.

"Yes, he wrote them both letters, explaining his reasoning," said Grandpa. "Then they planned the mission. They decided to fly out of Teller, Alaska, because of its proximity to Siberia. Earl Borland would fly along as Carl Ben's mechanic, and they would fly a Hamilton plane. Another pilot would be flying a Stinson, and unfortunately, this other pilot would be a *huge* problem later."

"Oh no!" said Kinley.

"So," Grandpa continued, "on the first flight to the *Nanuk*, which was about 500 miles, everything went well. They landed and six passengers got in Carl Ben's Hamilton plane, and 1,300 pounds of furs were put in the Stinson. Then they headed back to Alaska. On the way, they were caught in a blizzard in Siberia, but they were able to land in a native village, wait out the weather, and then return to Alaska safely."

Kinley looked a little frantic. "But something awful happens on the second flight, doesn't it?" she said.

"Unfortunately, yes," said Grandpa, his voice more quiet than usual. "It was time to head back to the *Nanuk* the second time, and that's where the problem occurred. The weather didn't cooperate, but that other pilot was the *biggest* problem."

"What do you mean?" asked Thomas.

"Well," replied Grandpa, "Carl Ben was smart enough and experienced enough to know that waiting for a little better weather was a wise thing, especially considering how dangerous it could be to fly through it. It was dangerous enough flying in this part of the world without taking big chances doing it in really bad weather. The other pilot was not as smart or experienced or patient as Carl Ben was, plus he was a braggart. He was sure he could fly through the weather no matter what, and he couldn't understand why Carl Ben was waiting around."

"So, does he convince Carl Ben to fly even though the weather was still bad?" asked Kinley.

"It's worse than that," said Grandpa. "On November 9, the other pilot took off for Siberia without even telling Carl Ben what he was doing … and what happened next was so tragic and sad. When Carl Ben realized the other plane had taken off, he decided that he had to follow … and you're not going to believe what happened. The other pilot returned not long after that and landed at Teller when he realized how bad the flying conditions were … but Carl Ben and Earl Borland didn't know that. They kept on flying."

Kinley closed her eyes and looked very sad. "And

the plane crashed," she said.

"Yes, it did," said Grandpa. "And Carl Ben and Earl Borland both died."

Grandpa, Kinley, and Thomas were quiet for several seconds. Kinley and Grandpa both got a tissue.

Thomas sighed. "That's really sad," he said, reaching for a tissue, "but Carl Ben sure had an incredible life, didn't he?"

"He sure did," said Kinley, sniffling. "But it always seemed like he lived on the edge."

"You're both right," said Grandpa. "The famous college football coach Lou Holtz was in Mandan many years ago, and he spoke to our Elks group and said something that I'll never forget. He said, 'Life is not measured by the number of breaths we take, but by the moments that take our breath away.' … Just think how many breathtaking moments the three of us have shared in our lives—and Carl Ben had a *bunch* of them packed into his 32 years on this earth. … Grandpa took a deep breath, smiled, and said, "But now, on a much happier note, I want to change the subject drastically and tell you what I have in mind. I think we've done a pretty good job learning about Carl Ben's life, but we might have missed something important. We also need to plan a summer adventure together when school's out."

"We're going to visit Carl Ben's house in Hatton!?" Kinley said excitedly.

"All *right*!" Thomas exclaimed.

"Yes, we are," said Grandpa. "I've got a friend who has a plane at the Mandan Airport, and I'll bet he will even fly us there. Then we can spend some quality time at Carl Ben's house, which I found out is now a museum."

"Can we visit Carl Ben's grave too?" asked Kinley.

"Of course, we can," said Grandpa. "It's not that far from the house."

Our Summer Adventure to Hatton

Written by Kinley

Edited with the help of Grandpa and Thomas
Photographed by Grandpa and Thomas

I originally started this to be a couple of pages in my diary, but after the exciting afternoon with Grandpa and Thomas flying to Hatton and visiting the home of Carl Ben Eielson, the famous North Dakota pilot, I decided to write more of an adventure story about the trip. I always love reading the stories Grandma wrote about her childhood adventures, so I decided to make this more of a story. I hope to author my own book of stories someday, so this adventure will make for a fun practice. I am glad I brought my notebook with to Hatton so I wouldn't forget anything important!

This is how the day started: It was Sunday, August 1 and the day for the trip had finally arrived. I heard Mother calling me to get up to get ready. I had already laid out my clothes for the day. I picked my Mandan Braves t-shirt, some comfy jeans, and my favorite sport shoes. I had my shoes broke in from all my hiking at Fort Abraham Lincoln State Park. Grandpa had told us there would be quite a bit of walking.

I made my bed, put away my toys. Thomas was already up and eating breakfast. Grandpa had said to eat a big breakfast, because we wouldn't get lunch until we got to Hatton. Secretly, I was a little too nervous and at the same time excited to eat very much.

I looked out the window and saw Grandpa coming up the sidewalk. The sky looked pretty with white fluffy clouds.

MANDAN AIRPORT W/JIM LAWLER SIGN; *AUTHOR PHOTO*

Grandpa came in our back door and gave Mother a hug. Then he high-fived Thomas and me. He was so excited about our adventure!

We got in Grandpa's car and headed toward the Mandan Airport. Grandpa brought his camera for some photos.

Grandpa drove out of Mandan and turned onto the road leading to the airport. We stopped to read the sign. Grandpa explained the Mandan Airport was renamed the Mandan Regional Airport – Lawler Field. He said the change was in memory of the last Airport Manager, Jim Lawler. Jim Lawler had started working there as a teenager.

We walked with Grandpa to look at the airport buildings. There was a small plane parked in front of a large building. I was surprised at the small airplane! I had only seen the large jets that flew over our house. Now I was feeling a little more nervous.

Mandan Airport w/Plane; *Author photo*

All of a sudden, I heard a plane flying around! Grandpa said that it looked like Mr. Logan's plane. It made a couple of circles and then came in for a landing.

We watched as the little plane landed with one bounce on the runway. Then the plane circled toward us and stopped. A young man with a big smile opened the side plane door and stepped out onto the pavement. He walked around the plane, then toward Grandpa, Thomas, and me.

He shook Grandpa's hand and fist bumped Thomas and me. He told us the air was smooth and the flight would be great. I was feeling a swirling in my stomach but decided not to tell anyone.

Mr. Logan wanted us to call him Logan. He asked us if we had ever been in a small plane before. I blurted out a big NO! Logan could tell I was a little nervous, so he tried to help me feel better. He said he was an airplane mechanic and a pilot. He not only flies planes but fixes them and would not fly a plane if it had any trouble.

Logan offered to let me sit in the front seat with him and if I was nervous about anything, he would be there.

Logan explained the plane we would be using was a Piper. I wrote that in my notebook, so I would not forget.

PIPER AIRPLANE; *AUTHOR PHOTO*

He helped Grandpa and Thomas get in the plane on the right side. They had to step up on the wing. Then we got in the plane. Logan showed us how to put on the headphones. Logan waited for all the instruments to show the plane was ready to take off. We took off smoothly from the airport, made a pass over Mandan. Logan said we would be flying for about one hour and twenty minutes to Hatton. There we would land on a grass runway!

After I flew for a little while, I was feeling much better. Grandpa was busy adjusting his camera and handed Thomas another camera to take photos out of the left-hand side of the plane. Logan and I talked about Carl Ben's adventures all the way to Hatton.

When I looked out of the plane window, the ground looked just like one of Grandma's block quilts. We passed by houses, barns, vehicles, and churches that looked like toys!

Church from the Plane; *Author photo*

Logan showed us the grass runway we were going to land on. I was thinking this was close to what Carl Ben may have experienced in Hatton. Logan flew around the town and dipped so Grandpa and Thomas could get some good photos of Hatton.

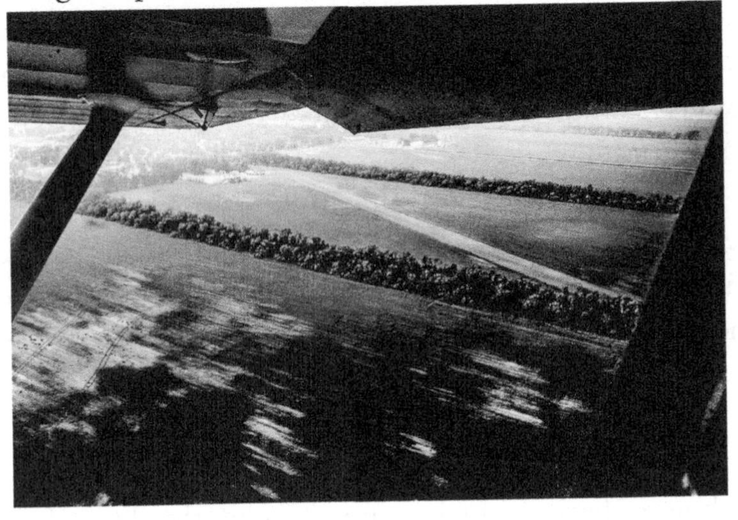

Hatton Grass Runway; *Author photo*

The first thing I saw when we flew over Hatton was the water tower with Hatton on it.

Hatton and Water Tower; *Author photo*

Logan flew us over the Carl Ben Eielson House. It looked so cool! I was so excited to see it, so Logan landed on the grass runway. By now I am too excited to be scared.

We got out of the plane and Logan said he had things to do and would be back to pick us up later.

Aerial Eielson Home; *Author photo*

Grandpa and Thomas were hungry, so we hiked to a local gas station and had some great pizza. Then we walked to find the house. There was a sign that showed us how to get there. I am glad I wore those good walking shoes!

The house was just a couple blocks from the sign. The first thing I thought when I saw the beautiful house was it was like an adult sized dollhouse. I could not wait to get inside and explore!

When you first come into the house, there is a winding staircase to the upstairs. There is a library, parlor, dining room and kitchen on the main floor. I didn't notice, but Grandpa noticed all the nice woodwork, fireplaces, and floors. Thomas noticed the huge piano and pump organ.

Eielson Museum Sign; *Author photo*

Carl Ben Eielson Museum; *Author photo*

Entry and Staircase; *Author photo*

Parlor and Fireplace; *Author photo*

Parlor and Piano; *Author photo*

Dining Room; *Author photo*

I walked through all the rooms downstairs before going upstairs. I noticed in the kitchen some stairs going up to the second floor. They looked secretive, like steps I read about in my favorite Nancy Drew mystery books. A guide who was there to answer any questions said they were for the servants, who did not use the main stairs.

Servant Staircase; *Author photo*

I also notice another strange thing in the kitchen. It was called a "dumbwaiter". The guide said this was to hand the servant in the dining room the food hot from the kitchen without the cook walking into the dining room. Whoa! The Eielson family must have been rich! When I left the kitchen, I saw a huge stove. Grandpa said it used wood to cook with and had a tank for hot water. It looked far more complicated than our microwave!

Dumbwaiter in the Kitchen; *Author photo*

It was time for me to explore the upstairs, but first I went back to the library and looked at all the photos and interesting maps on the walls. There were many books and articles about Carl Ben and his family. I am so glad Grandpa told us the story so well on Blizzard Day!

Finally, it was time for me to explore the upstairs. I was so curious about what was in the tower of the house. From the outside, we could see the shape of a lady on the top floor through the window. Grandpa said that the tower was called a "turret". When we got to the second floor, it was full of many different historical items from the community as well as the Eielson family things. One room had a bedroom set and another a sewing room of many different fashions.

Dumbwaiter in the Dining Room; *Author photo*

Kitchen Stove; *Author photo*

LIBRARY ROOM; *AUTHOR PHOTO*

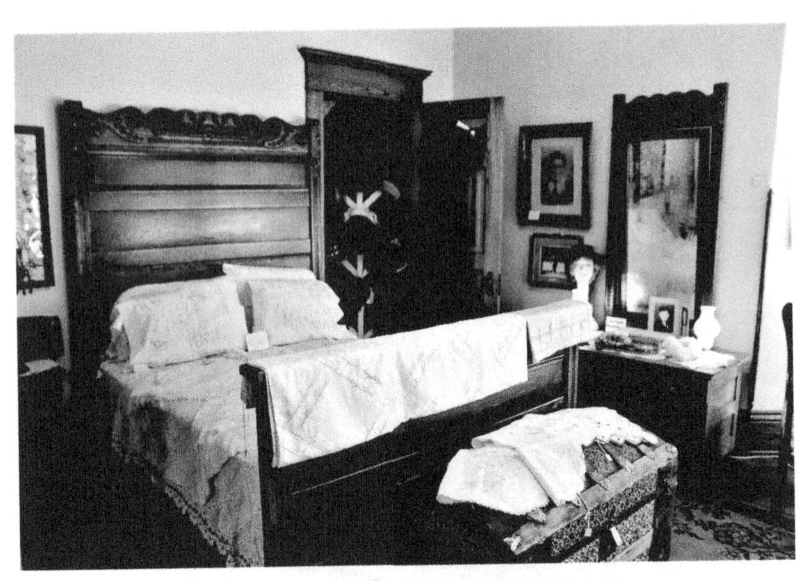

MASTER BEDROOM, 2ND FLOOR; *AUTHOR PHOTO*

Sewing Room, 2nd Floor; *Author photo*

Next, I went up the stairs to the attic. Attics have always been mysterious to me. Many times, they contain old trunks and secrets. This attic was full of more things from Hatton's history.

Eielson Trunk, Attic; *Author photo*

This attic held the secret to the tower room, I mean, turret. It was a replica of an old school room. The mannequin in the corner was the teacher. The alphabet in cursive was around the top of the room. When you looked up to the tower, it was like a large ice cream cone.

CORNER CLASSROOM, ATTIC; *AUTHOR PHOTO*

I was also told by the guide; the Eielson children would play basketball in the attic. I could have spent a week in that house looking at all the stained-glass windows and nooks and crannies. I heard Grandpa and Thomas calling for me. They had finished looking through the house and were anxious to get to the hangar to see one of Carl Ben's airplanes. I ran down the stairs and found them waiting on the big porch.

Tower View, Attic; *Karen Berg photo*

The Eielson Attic; *Author photo*

Down the Staircase; *Author photo*

The Eielson Porch; *Author photo*

Grandpa and Thomas led the way to the hangar. Our guide was already there ready to open the door. The hangar used to house the plane was just a couple blocks away from the home. This was the part THEY were excited to see!

We went into the building and looked at the plane, the wings were off for storage, but there were many pictures and stories about Carl Ben here too. Grandpa and Thomas took lots of pictures of the plane inside and out.

CARL BEN EIELSON HANGAR FRONT; *AUTHOR PHOTO*

Grandpa and Thomas read the sign about the plane out loud.

Grandpa and Thomas circled the plane over and over making comments like "I can't believe this flew!" and "The steering wheels look like they came from an old car!"

Carl Ben Eielson Hangar Side; *Author photo*

Airplane Description Sign; *Author photo*

Front of Airplane with Engine; *Author photo*

Sideview of Plane with Windows; *Author photo*

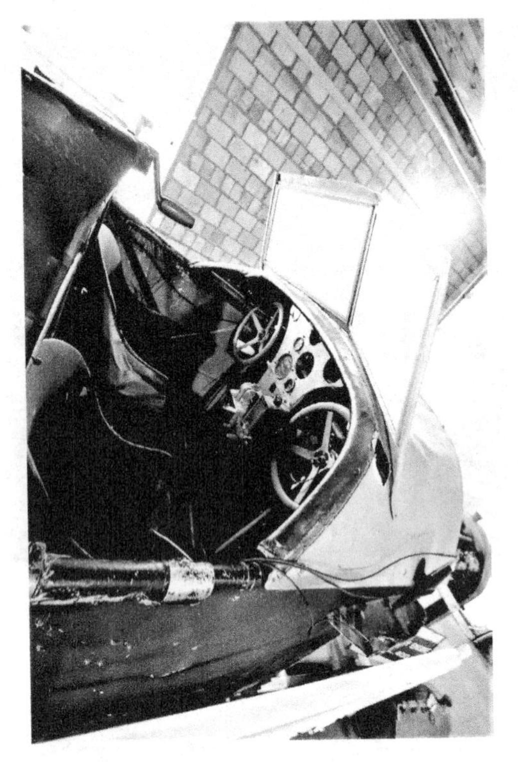

PLANE COCKPIT; *AUTHOR PHOTO*

TAIL OF PLANE; *AUTHOR PHOTO*

I walked around the plane too, but I began to think of what Carl Ben had done with the plane. He flew crazy! Barnstorming and tricks!

I came to a display that made me very sad. First, there was a telegram telling the family about the crash. In another frame, there were some newspaper stories about the crash that happened to Carl Ben, with some pieces from the plane.

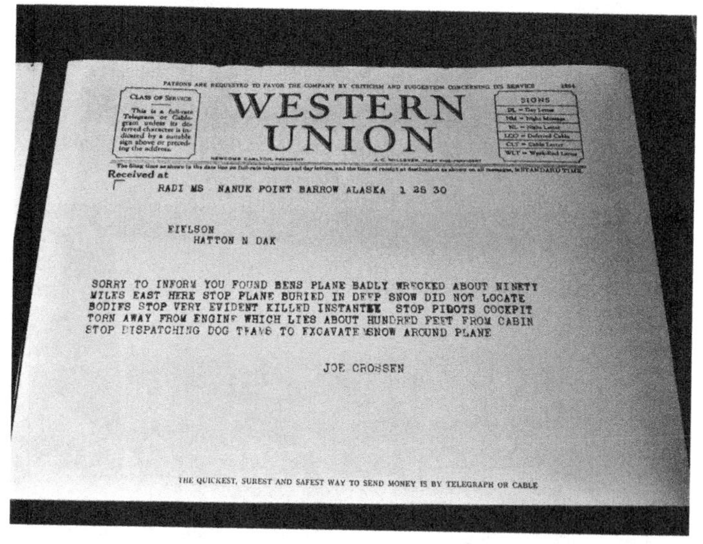

PATRONS ARE REQUESTED TO FAVOR THE COMPANY BY CRITICISM AND SUGGESTION CONCERNING ITS SERVICE

CLASS OF SERVICE

This is a full-rate Telegram or Cablegram unless its deferred character is indicated by a suitable sign above or preceding the address.

WESTERN UNION

SIGNS

DL = Day Letter
NM = Night Message
NL = Night Letter
LCO = Deferred Cable
CLT = Cable Letter
WLT = Week-End Letter

Received at

RADI MS NANUK POINT BARROW ALASKA 1 28 30

FIELSON
HATTON N DAK

SORRY TO INFORM YOU FOUND BENS PLANE BADLY WRECKED ABOUT NINETY MILES EAST HERE STOP PLANE BURIED IN DEEP SNOW DID NOT LOCATE BODIES STOP VERY EVIDENT KILLED INSTANTLY STOP PILOTS COCKPIT TORN AWAY FROM ENGINE WHICH LIES ABOUT HUNDRED FEET FROM CABIN STOP DISPATCHING DOG TEAMS TO EXCAVATE SNOW AROUND PLANE

JOE CROSSEN

THE QUICKEST, SUREST AND SAFEST WAY TO SEND MONEY IS BY TELEGRAPH OR CABLE

TELEGRAM OF CARL BEN CRASH; *AUTHOR PHOTO*

While Grandpa and Thomas were discussing the airplane in the hangar, I started to cry. The guide handed me a Kleenex and said she cries too. We looked at a framed photo of Carl Ben's funeral that showed over 5,000 people attended it. I felt better then, knowing he had so many friends.

Grandpa came over and gave me a hug. Thomas felt sad too. Grandpa said we had the longest hike of the day ahead of us and we had to go.

CARL BEN CRASH STORY WITH PIECES OF AIRPLANE; *AUTHOR PHOTO*

CARL BEN'S FUNERAL, ST JOHN'S LUTHERAN CHURCH; *AUTHOR PHOTO*

We needed to go up the highway to see the memorial and cemetery of Carl Ben and the Eielson family. We walked and talked about everything we had seen so far. We finally reached the large memorial. It showed again how much everyone cared for Carl Ben.

St. John's Lutheran Church; *Author photo*

Carl Ben Eielson Memorial Arch; *Author Photo*

CARL BEN EIELSON FAMILY PLOT; *AUTHOR PHOTO*

CARL BEN EIELSON GRAVESTONE; *KAREN BERG PHOTO*

Aerial Photo 1, Carl Ben Eielson Memorial;
Author Photo

Aerial Photo 2, Carl Ben Eielson Memorial;
Author Photo

Aerial Photo 1, Hatton; *Author Photo*

Aerial Photo 2, Hatton; *Author Photo*

I heard a plane flying over the cemetery and looked up and saw Logan coming in for a landing on the grass airstrip. Grandpa told us to hurry back to the airstrip to meet up with Logan. He was ready to take us back to Mandan. We hurried to the airstrip and got back in the plane with Logan. This time I was excited for the ride back and had lots of things to share with him about what I had learned.

Logan told Grandpa he would fly around Hatton and the memorial again so we could get a few more photos. That was fun as we dipped and went around the town. We waved goodbye to the town of Hatton as we zoomed by! Grandpa said he was going to put a photo album together of our Summer Adventure!

We landed safely in Mandan. I asked Logan about how to learn to fly an airplane. After seeing what Carl Ben did so long ago, Carl Ben is my new hero and I want to be like him when I grow up! I want to not be afraid and try do something good for others like Carl Ben did on his last flight.

Logan is my new friend and offered to take us flying again sometime! He calmed my fears and showed me that small planes are fun and useful!

Most of all, Grandpa is my BESTEST Grandpa. He always teaches Thomas and me something new! This week we went to the Capitol Building in Bismarck to see the Carl Ben Eielson painting hanging in the Hall of Fame.

I can't wait for our next Blizzard Day!

CARL BEN EIELSON PHOTO IN THE THEODORE ROOSEVELT ROUGH RIDER HALL OF FAME, STATE CAPITOL, BISMARCK; *AUTHOR PHOTO*

Making Great Aunt Karol's Chocolate Chip Cookies

Kinley and Thomas finished washing their hands, then joined Grandpa by the kitchen counter. The electric mixer was there, along with the chocolate chip cookie recipe card and all the ingredients they would need.

"OK," said Grandpa. "Here we go. Thomas, you can turn the oven on to 375."

"Will do," said Thomas, walking over to the oven. "Done!" he said when he was finished.

"Very good," said Grandpa. "Now, I'll let you two measure the first ingredients and put them in the bowl."

"Butter first," said Kinley.

"That's right," said Grandpa. "We need two-thirds of a cup of butter, and that's about ten and two-thirds tablespoons on this butter stick." He handed the butter stick to Kinley. "I didn't have time to set it out, so you can cut the stick up into pieces and put them into the bowl."

Kinley went over to the small cutting board nearby and cut the butter stick up, then returned and pushed the pieces into the mixing bowl with the knife. Grandpa started the mixer at a low speed. After that, Kinley and Thomas took turns putting some more ingredients in the bowl. They were: two-thirds of a cup of shortening, one cup of granulated sugar, and one cup of brown sugar, packed.

"Excellent," said Grandpa when they'd finished. "Now we'll mix these together on high before we add anything else."

Kinley turned the mixer on high for a few minutes

and they watched the ingredients mix up really well.

"Okay," said Grandpa, "now we're going to put two eggs and two teaspoons of vanilla in there."

Thomas put two teaspoons of vanilla in the bowl. Grandpa cracked the two eggs and added them to the other ingredients, and they mixed everything up thoroughly on high.

After that was done, Grandpa said, "Now Kinley, you need to turn the mixer down to *low* before we add the baking soda, salt, and flour."

Kinley turned the mixer down to *low*.

"I'll put in the one teaspoon of baking soda and one teaspoon of salt," said Thomas, and he added them to the bowl.

"I'll do the three cups of Gold Medal flour," said Kinley, as she added them to the mixing bowl, one cup at a time.

After a few minutes, Grandpa said, "All right. Turn off the mixer, Kinley."

Kinley turned off the mixer. Grandpa touched the dough and said, "It seems a little sticky. Let's add another half cup of flour or so."

Thomas poured in another half cup of flour, and Grandpa checked the dough again.

"That's excellent," he said. "Now, let's add the package of semisweet chocolate chips."

"I'll take care of that," said Kinley, as she poured in the chocolate chips from the open bag nearby.

"Thomas," said Grandpa, "now you can mix them in there with the spatula."

Thomas mixed the chocolate chips into the dough. "That's excellent," Grandpa said when Thomas was done.

"Now, let's go over to the kitchen table. You two can put rounded balls of cookie dough, about two teaspoons full each, on the parchment paper I put on the cookie sheets. Put them about two inches apart."

Kinley and Thomas took their time putting the rounded balls of cookie dough on the cookie sheets.

"Grandpa," asked Thomas, "where did you get this recipe again?"

"Your great aunt Karol Volk gave it to me," he answered. "She's got the reputation for making the best chocolate chip cookies anywhere, and no one seems to be able to make them quite as good as she does."

"I can't believe she makes them any better than you, Grandpa," said Kinley. "They're the best!"

"Yeah, Grandpa," Thomas added.

"Well, thanks," said Grandpa with a big smile. "With all your help, I think these will be our best *ever*! Great Aunt Karol always says that the secret to her cookies is putting plenty of love into making them, and I think we're doing that."

"We sure are, Grandpa," said Thomas.

When Kinley and Thomas had finished putting all the rounded balls of cookie dough on the parchment paper, Grandpa said, "That's perfect! Now, Great Aunt Karol says the recipe calls for eight to ten minutes of baking, but I've found they usually take about ten to twelve minutes to bake. Set the timer for nine minutes, and we'll take a peek in the oven when it goes off."

Thomas put a pan of unbaked cookies in the oven.

About the Author *** Paulette Bullinger

Paulette Bullinger is interested in North Dakota history and the people who led remarkable lives in her home state.

Paulette grew up in Huff, a very small town in North Dakota. Her interests are writing, photography and exploring North Dakota back roads.

Paulette's first book, *Nothing Hidden,* is a historical fiction mystery set in the Bismarck area.

Paulette also leads local history walking tours of downtown Bismarck and the St. Mary's Cemetery.

Paulette and her husband, Bob, live in Bismarck and are the proud parents of seven children and grandparents to nine grandchildren.

Tosha Rochelle Photography, Bismarck

About the Author *** Kevin Kremer

Kevin Kremer first heard about Carl Ben Eielson when he did an author visit to the elementary school named in Eielson's honor on the Grand Forks Air Force Base in North Dakota. After that, Kremer learned that the first airport in his hometown of Mandan was also named after Carl Ben Eielson. It was then that Carl Ben's story was put on Kremer's list of Possible Future Books to Write.

Kremer grew up in Mandan, North Dakota, and he loves to write books involving that area. He also likes to include his favorite places in Mandan in his writing—including Ohm's Cafe and A&B Pizza and Frieds Family Restaurant.

Dr. Kremer has written, edited, and published more than 100 books, and he loves writing children's books the most. Kremer also likes helping other authors with challenges they are having with their own book projects.

Kremer has a writing-publishing company to help people with book projects of any kind. To contact him regarding book or e-book projects, school author visits, or to purchase books, go to:

Web site: **KevinKremerBooks.com**
E-mail: **snowinsarasota@aol.com**
Facebook: **Kevin Kremer Books and North Dakota's Polar Pilot!**

Nothing tops sauerkraut and Canadian bacon pizza at A&B Pizza

Kremer enjoying the world's best hamburgers at Ohm's Cafe

BRUINS
Carl Ben
Eielson
Middle School

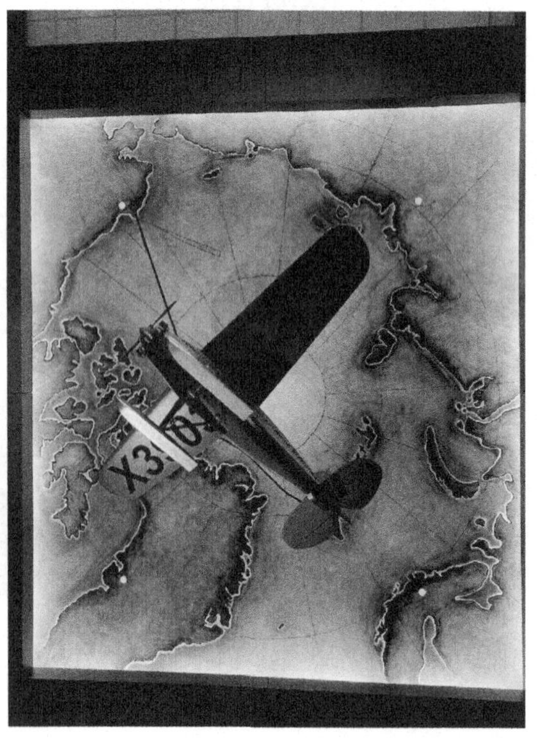

Photos from Carl Ben Eielson Middle School in Fargo, North Dakota, taken by Miranda Dietrich

To arrange for a reasonably priced author visit or to buy other great books go to:
KevinKremerBooks.com

Published by Kremer Publishing
2022
P.O. Box 1385
Osprey, FL 34229-1385